TEMPLE ON A HILL

TEMPLE ON A HILL

The Building of the Parthenon

ANNE ROCKWELL

Atheneum 1969 New York

Library of Congress catalog card number 71-75520
Published simultaneously in Canada
by McClelland and Stewart Ltd.
Manufactured in the United States of America
by Kingsport Press, Inc., Kingsport, Tennessee
Designed by Judith Lerner
First Edition

for
Hannah
Elizabeth & Oliver

ONE

THE PERSIANS were coming again to Greece. Eight years earlier, in 490 B.C. the citizens of the city-state of Athens had driven Darius, the Great King of the Persians, from their land at a battle on the crescent-shaped meadow at Marathon. Darius never came again; he died five years after the battle of Marathon. But he had been succeeded by his even more ambitious son, Xerxes. And now, Xerxes was making his way across the lands that lay on the eastern side of the Mediterranean Sea, demanding of each city that he approached tokens of absolute submission to his rule: a bowl of earth and water. City after city gave him the tokens, and across the sea in Athens the citizens were afraid that soon earth and water would be demanded of them also. The military power behind Xerxes was vast; a small city-state like Athens had little hope of resisting him.

But there was always a chance. So a messenger was sent from Athens to the sacred oracle at Delphi for advice. All of the Greek-speaking people believed that Delphi was the holiest spot on earth, for it was thought that at that place lay the very center of the earth. There, in a temple, the Pythoness, who was the priestess of the oracle, sang out secret and holy sayings that priests interpreted. No one else could understand the sayings. The Athenian messenger asked the Pythoness to tell him what his people should do to protect themselves from Xerxes. Her counsel was dismal indeed.

She described a city burned to the ground, a city where black blood poured through the streets from the roofs of the temples. "Flee! Flee!" she cried; but she did not tell where on earth the Athenians might go to be safe from the invading Persians. The messenger brought this sad news back to Athens.

The citizens listened to the prophecy, but were not content with it. They could not accept the idea that their beloved city would be destroyed. When they discussed it among themselves, they decided that perhaps they had been too abrupt with the Pythoness and had forgotten their manners in dealing with the sacred oracle. So, in hope of better tidings, the council of citizens chosen to act on such matters sent the messenger back to Delphi. This time he did not go empty-handed; he brought generous gifts to the temple and carried olive boughs as a sign of supplication.

In response, the Pythoness did prophesy again, and this time she held out a hint of hope. Still the temples would burn, still the black blood would flow, but for those who hid behind a wall of wood, salvation waited. She also spoke of the island of Salamis, near Athens.

She referred to it as "Holy Salamis" and called it the place where many mothers' sons would die. No one understood what she meant.

In the market place, or *agora,* of Athens, where the men met for business and conversation each day, no one talked of anything but what the Delphic oracle had said. What, and where, was the "wall of wood," and what had the island of Salamis to do with them? At the fountain house where the women met each morning to fill their water jugs, they too talked of the wooden wall and Salamis. What did it mean? Athens was a city built of limestone and sun-dried brick, and nowhere was there a wooden wall. And whose sons were fated to die at Salamis? Why did the gods play such tricks on men?

Meanwhile, even as Xerxes prepared to conquer them, good luck came to the citizens of Athens. In 482 B.C. a rich vein of silver was discovered in a silver mine that belonged to the city. The citizens wanted to distribute the money from the silver equally among them, and the council agreed that this would be fair. But there was one man who disagreed. His name was Themistocles, and he was one of the outstanding political leaders of Athens.

Like all Athenians, Themistocles had pondered long and hard on the words of the oracle. And he believed that, at last, he understood them. He interpreted the wall of wood to be a fleet of long ships that could do battle against Xerxes, and he also believed that only in the enclosed harbor of Salamis could the Athenian navy defeat the oncoming ships of Xerxes. The vein of silver was, he believed, something the gods had sent to fulfill the prophecy; for although the money, distributed among all the citizens, could make each man only a little more prosperous (and what would this matter once the Persians came?), as a lump sum it was enough to build a good-sized navy. The problem Themistocles faced was how to persuade the citizens to vote for such a thing. They were a free-thinking lot, and it would not be easy to make them act together, as one mind, even to save themselves.

Themistocles was no gentleman with elegant manners. In fact, many people considered him a boor, and even his closest friends wondered why he did not master a musical instrument or learn to recite a little poetry, as most well-to-do Athenian men did. When someone scornfully asked him why he did not play the lyre, he answered that this did not interest him. Rather, he said, if he were given a small and insignificant city of citizens free to make their own choices, he could play upon that city more beautifully than any man could upon the lyre. He could make it great and glorious.

And what he said was true. For Themistocles was clever and wily; his business was human nature, which he understood well. When he spoke about the navy, he came right to the point; he passed through the streets of Athens, talking to men who worked on the docks at the neighboring port of Piraeus, to farmers who came to market, to merchants who sent their olive-oil laden cargo ships around the Mediterranean Sea, and to the shepherds who came down from the mountains. He warned them of the terrible things that could happen if they were conquered by Xerxes, and he convinced them that they should do as he said. Before long citizens of all classes chose to take the proceeds of the silver mine and build with it Themistocles' wall of wood.

Work began. The ships were to be of a comparatively new design, one that is thought to have been invented in the Greek city of Corinth about fifty years before. They were called *triremes* because they were rowed in battle by three groups of oarsmen. This probably gave the ships great speed and mobility. But no one knows for sure, because no one knows today just what triremes were like for no ancient triremes, or even pictures of them, have ever been found. No one knows, for example, exactly how the oarsmen sat. Some people today say that they were placed on benches, one above

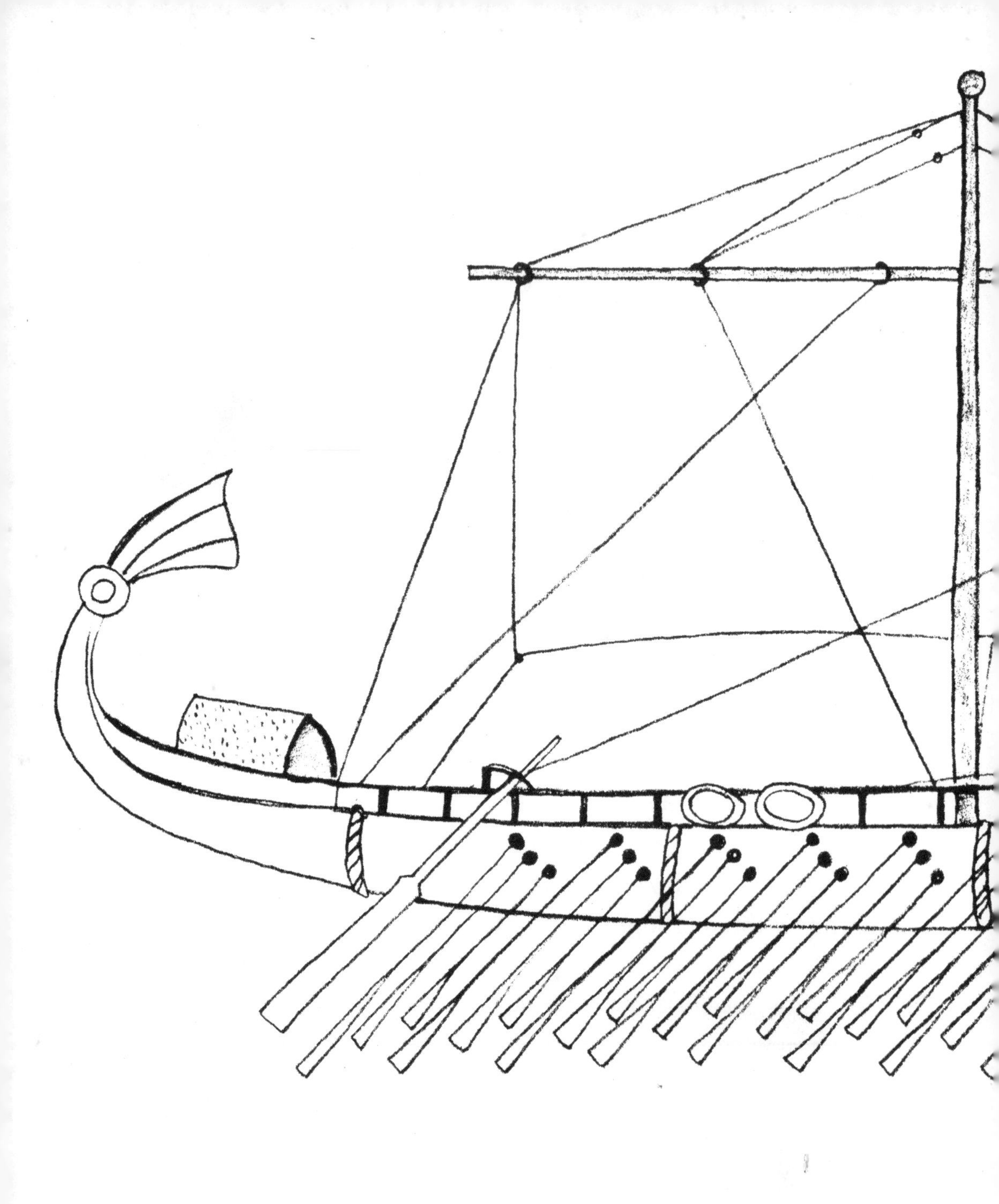

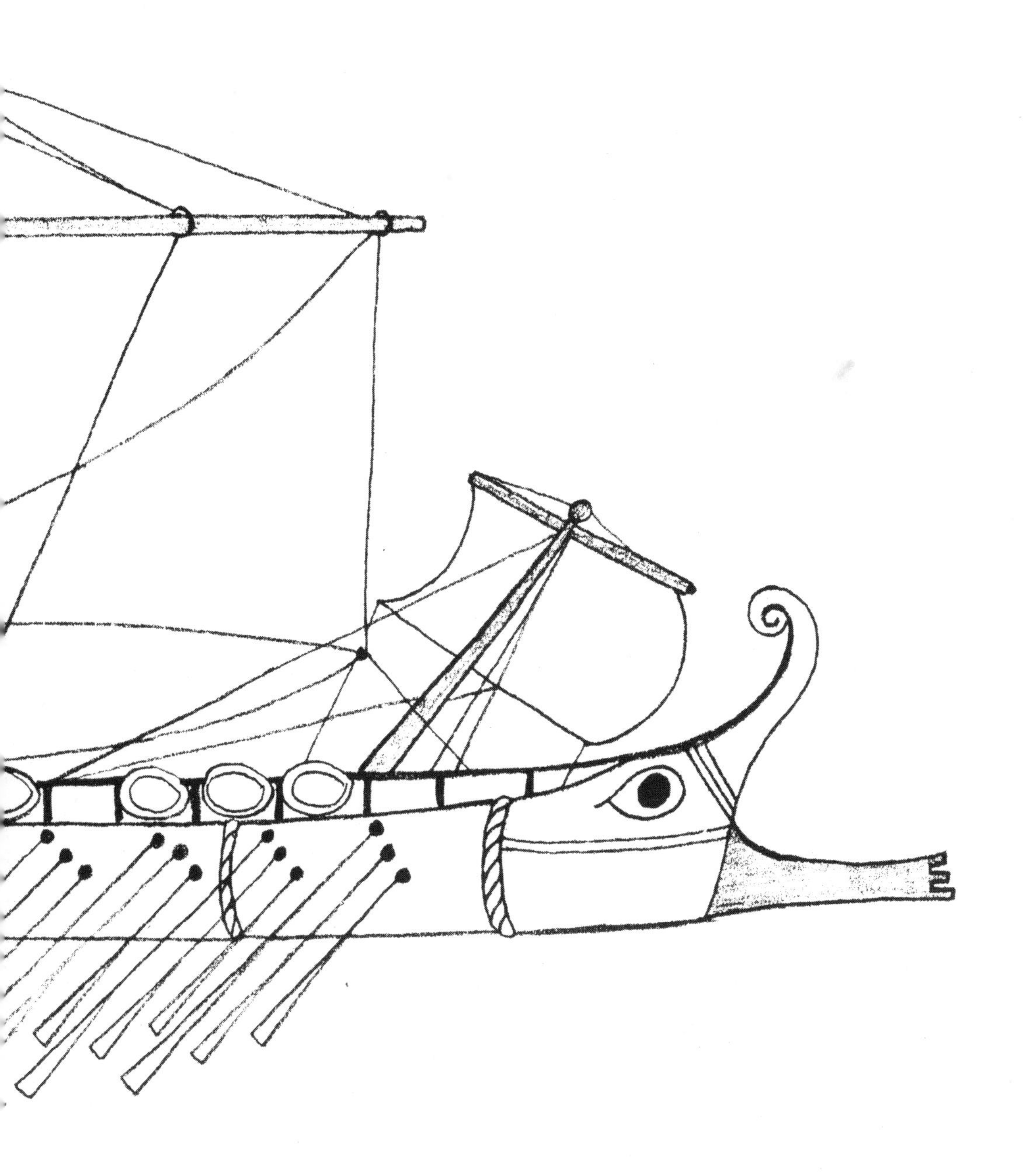

How A Trireme May Have Looked

the other, while others say that they sat in groups of three men in a row on one bench.

Triremes were large as ships of that time went. They were probably about 125 feet long by about 20 feet wide. The scraggly mountain pines and firs from the sparse slopes around the city were felled. The trees were cut into lumber and the boards curved and shaped and held together with bronze nails until they formed a long and graceful hull. The keel, running beneath the length of the hull, was built of hardest oak, so that the ship would not be damaged when it was dragged, with its keel touching ground, over rocky beaches. The planking for the decks and the rower's benches was made of many softer woods. There was one tall pine mast, carrying a large, bright colored linen sail. This sail was used to power the ship on long voyages, in order to save the energy of the rowers for battle. Because the mast was tall and cumbersome, it was made so that it could be removed and beached before a battle. There was a second short mast, with a little sail. This sail was used for short journeys, and unlike the large one, it was a permanent part of the ship.

After the ship was built, but before it was placed in the water, all of the seams were caulked with a mixture of tar and straw to keep the water out. Then, the entire exterior of the ship was painted with melted wax containing bright-colored pigments. At the bow, looking straight ahead, was a large, painted eye, to guide the ship through any sea.

Below the eye—jutting straight out into the water—was a piece of timber sheathed with bronze. This was the weapon with which the great trireme fought. Its only purpose was to ram a hole into an enemy ship and disable her. The triremes were girded around the hull in several places with strong cables made of flax, so that the ship would not crack under the impact of ramming into another ship.

In less than two years, which was a short time in those days when all work was done by hand, the "wall of wood" was built. There were probably two hundred ships, each requiring a crew of more than two hundred men, one hundred and seventy of whom were rowers. Unlike rowers on ships of other lands at the time, the Athenian rowers were not slaves. They were citizens who were too poor to equip themselves with armor for fighting on land. They were offered high pay with generous bonuses for their services, and they soon filled the trireme rowing benches.

It was none too soon. In the beginning of the year 480 B.C. Xerxes was making ready to march from Asia to Europe. He had collected a vast army under his command; and while his messengers traveled to the various cities of Greece, demanding earth and water for their king, his engineers were building a bridge more than a mile long across the Hellespont. This was the strait between the Aegean Sea and the Sea of Marmara, which separated Asia from Europe. As soon as the bridge was completed, Xerxes planned to march his armies across it.

The Greeks had a reprieve when the bridge collapsed in a storm before it was finished. Xerxes, in fury, chopped off the heads of the engineers who had built it, and went, himself, to the shores of the Hellespont. He cursed the strait, called it foul and briny, branded it with his red-hot branding irons until it steamed and sizzled, then last of all commanded his guards to give the uncooperative water three hundred lashes with their long whips. Finally, when the engineers and the Hellespont had been sufficiently punished, he commanded new engineers to begin again.

This time the engineers were successful. Mighty triremes, and their smaller sisters, the fifty-oared penteconters, were anchored in the strait and tied fast to one another. From this continuous row of ships spanning the water, the engineers and workmen built the bridge. This second bridge was built with cables, some of flax and some of papyrus. Across the cables, wide wooden planks were placed, one after the other. In a short time the work was done; and from the city of Sardis, in Asia Minor, Xerxes commanded his armies to begin their march.

There lived at this time, in the city of Halicarnassus on the Eastern Shore of the Aegean Sea, a boy named Herodotus. When he became a man, he wrote down the history of the war between Xerxes and the Greek-speaking people. Much of what we know of it today, we know from him. These are some of the people Herodotus tells us marched with King Xerxes:

First there were the Persians themselves, with their allies and closely related peoples, the Medes. They dressed in long trousers and wore shirts of overlapping pieces of clanking iron that resembled the scales of a fish. Their weapons were short spears and giant bows and long, sharp daggers hanging from their thighs. To protect themselves they carried shields of woven straw, or wicker.

There were Indians in crisp, cotton dresses. Arabians rode swift camels and wore long, flowing cloaks. There were the Ethiopians, who painted their bodies with red earth and white chalk, and who looked fierce and splendid in their skins of leopards and lions, carrying spears of polished antelope horn. Then, there were Libyans, from deep in Africa. These people wore helmets made of the scalped heads of horses, with ears standing high and manes blowing in the breeze. Their dresses were of leather, made something like those the Indians wore; they carried iron spears and shields made of the skins of cranes.

There were Scythians, in high, pointed caps. And there were men from the wild, high meadows of Thrace, with fox-skins on their heads and bright-colored cloaks streaming down their backs. Their legs were wrapped in the soft skins of fawns, and they carried long, sharp javelins, like those of the Greeks.

These were only some of the many who made up the army of Xerxes. On horseback, on camel-back, in chariots drawn by high-stepping horses, in wagons pulled by fast wild donkeys, by ox-cart, and on foot, they moved toward the Hellespont. They were accompanied by baggage bearers, mules, cooks, women to grind their flour, and even dogs. No one knows their number; Herodotus tells us that the army amounted to one million seven hundred thousand men, with more than that number in hangers-on. Most historians today think he exaggerated, but no one knows how many there *really* were. Everyone is sure that there were at least three hundred thousand soldiers.

As Xerxes and his army neared the Hellespont, drinking, so it was said, entire rivers dry, his navy, made up principally of Egyptians and Phoenicians, sailed toward the Hellespont from ports on the southern and eastern shores of the Mediterranean. Most of the ships were triremes, probably similar to those that were rapidly being completed by the Athenians, but some were penteconters. Probably Herodotus is also exaggerating when he tells us that there were one thousand, two hundred and seven triremes alone in the navy of Xerxes; but again, no one knows exactly how many there were. The number is thought to be closer to eight hundred. In any case, there were many more ships in this navy than in the one Themistocles was building, and there were more than had ever been seen in any sea together before.

While the Persians and their allies advanced by land and sea, the Greeks made plans. Although there was no nation of Greece, and, in fact, the small city-states had little in common and often fought among themselves, they were, nevertheless united by a common language and a belief in the same gods. Athens and Sparta, the two most powerful Greek city-states, forgot, for the time being, their long-standing differences; for they saw that they must work together if they were to remain independent. A plan was drawn up. Sparta, under the direction of her king, Leonidas, would send an army of about six thousand Greeks eastward to meet King Xerxes and fight him in the narrow pass at

Route of Xerxes

Thermopylae. Here the Persians would be at a disadvantage, because they would have to form a narrow column to push their way through the gorge, between the steep cliffs. In such a place the Greeks would have at least half a chance. While the army of Leonidas was fighting on land, a navy of Athenian and other Greek ships would fight the Persian navy in the sea near the pass.

When Xerxes reached Thermopylae, Leonidas and his army were waiting for him. Xerxes sent a spy to see what the Greeks were up to, and to find out how many there were. When the spy looked down into the long gorge, he could hardly believe what he saw. Here was an army a fraction of the size of the one Xerxes was leading, and it was, to the Persian spy, behaving in a most un-warlike fashion.

Some of the young soldiers were gaily performing graceful acrobatic tricks, while others sat calmly around their campfires combing and braiding their long, shining hair. When the spy reported these strange doings to King Xerxes, the king laughed and called for a man named Demaratus. Demaratus was Spartan, but he had committed a crime and had been exiled from his native city. Turning traitor, he had offered his services to Xerxes as a sort of advisor on what his people were like. Xerxes had the spy tell Demaratus what he had seen; but unlike the king, Demaratus did not laugh. He told Xerxes that this was a sign that the Spartans were there to fight to the death. For, he said, it was an ancient custom of his people for a soldier to braid and dress his hair more perfectly and more beautifully than he had ever done before, on the eve of a battle in which he was likely to die. Demaratus told the king that victory for the Persians was by no means certain. When Xerxes reminded Demaratus of how outnumbered the Greeks were, Demaratus warned the king that these men were like no others he had ever fought, and that no one could be sure of winning in a battle against determined Spartans, whatever the odds might be.

It was true. The Spartans were a brave and warlike people. Each Spartan boy was raised from the age of seven to be a warrior. He was taught to suffer any amount of physical pain without flinching, and he learned to live a gaunt and austere life. Even the girls were taught to fight, for it was thought that only by being like soldiers themselves, could they be fit mothers for young Spartan braves. Weak and sickly babies and children were left on the windy mountainsides to die, for Sparta tolerated no weakness among her people. Their king, Leonidas, was braver than their bravest and was said to be a descendant of the great hero of Greek mythology, Hercules himself.

But Xerxes could not believe that this puny army was doing more than toying with him, and for four days he refused to fight, hoping that by so doing, the Spartans would just pack up and go home. But they did not, and on the fifth day the Persians attacked; the battle began.

It was soon apparent that Demaratus had known what he was talking about; for while the men of Xerxes' army were certainly more numerous, they were no match for the skilled Greek warriors. One after another the Persians fell dead in the narrow pass of Thermopylae. On the second day of fighting it began to look as if the Greeks would hold the pass and drive the Persians back. Then Xerxes ordered his bravest soldiers, an elite corps called "The Ten Thousand," to climb the cliff after dark, guided by a traitorous Greek who knew the countryside, and ambush the Greeks from behind.

That night, the Greeks were awakened by a strange sound. Silently and fearfully they listened until they were certain of what they heard. Through the deep oak forests lying above the narrow gorge they heard the rustling of many little leaves, as though a gentle wind were blowing among them . . . nothing more. But, they guessed that it was the Persians, creeping through the forest, and they knew that they were doomed.

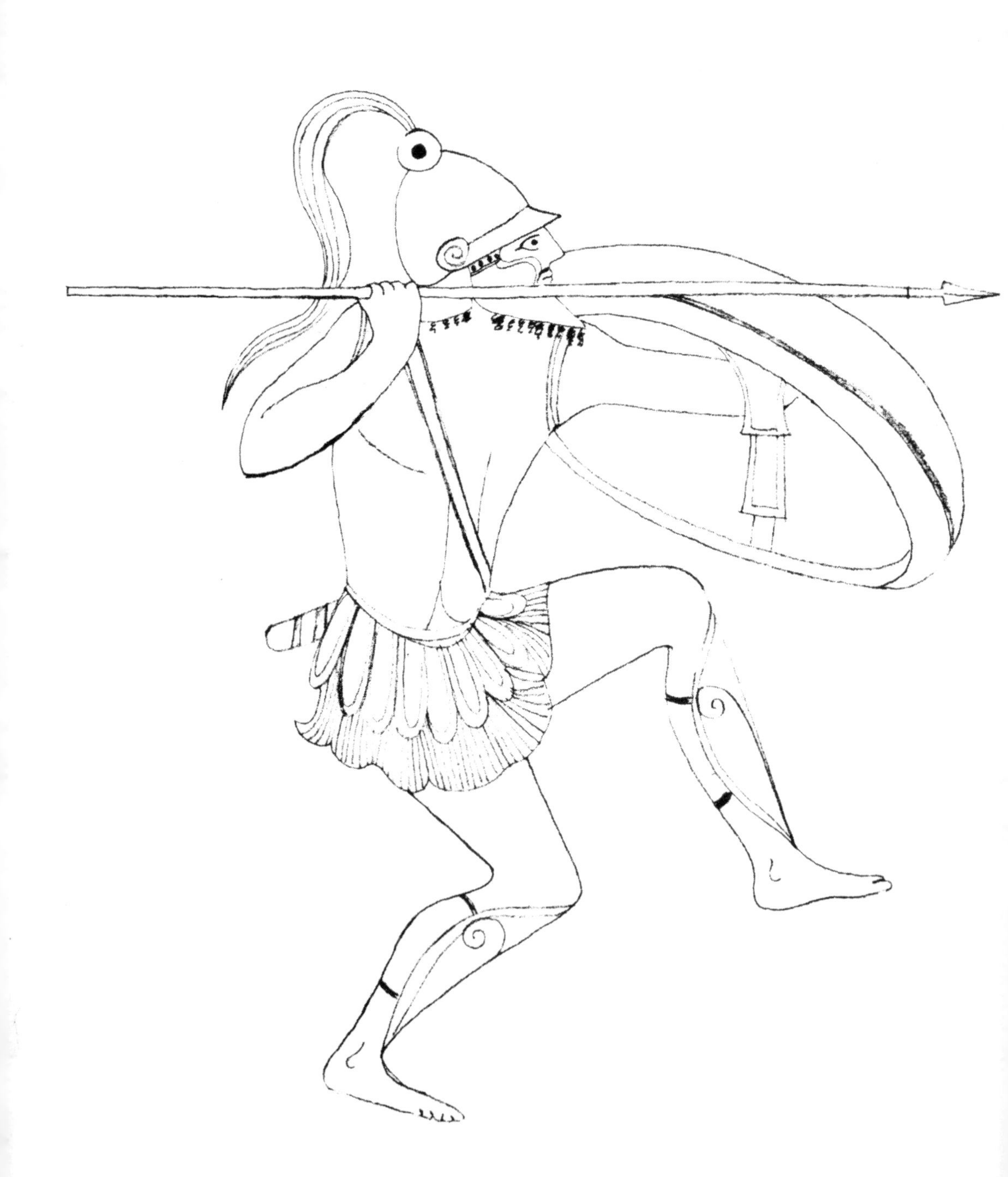

For some reason, no one understands why, all of the Greeks but Leonidas and three hundred Spartans chosen by him, left Thermopylae. Some say they deserted; some say they were sent by Leonidas to fight the Persians up ahead in another more favorable spot. Whatever the reason might have been, they left and no one now will ever know why.

When morning came, one of the Spartans reported to Leonidas on the size of the Persian army he had seen approaching at the rear of the pass. He described it as so vast that its flying arrows would hide even the sun. But to this terrible news, a Spartan soldier named Dienekes only answered: "Good. Then we shall fight in the shade." For it was a hot day in July.

They fought in the shade; all were killed. And most of the Greeks who had departed were overtaken by the Persians and also killed. Four thousand Greek soldiers fell that day to Xerxes, and his army marched on.

But with the Athenians in the waters off Thermopylae, things were different. Before sailing to the bay where they would meet the Persian navy, the Athenians had again consulted the Delphic oracle. The oracle advised them to sacrifice to Boreas, serpent-tailed god of the North Wind, and he would favor them. On many altars along the coast, the Athenians faithfully offered the gilded thigh bone of a fresh-killed bull and the first draught of their finest wine to Boreas, and Boreas accepted their gifts. Herodotus tells of a great tempest with violent waves and high winds that churned up the waters where the Persian navy sailed, sinking four hundred of their triremes; but none of the Greek ships were lost. Before the Athenians set sail for home, they poured libations of their finest wine into the salty sea as a thank offering to Poseidon, God of the Sea, who had cooperated so generously with Boreas on their behalf.

TWO

THE GREEK FLEET returned home unharmed, but with the knowledge that the vast army that had destroyed the defense at Thermopylae was marching towards Athens. The Athenians also knew that the great Persian navy would recover from its loss and still outnumber them. Themistocles, remembering well the dire prophecy of the Delphic oracle, gave orders that all women, children, old people and slaves should leave the city and go to the island of Salamis and the coastal town of Troezen. Most people left, but there were a few who put their trust, not in Themistocles' wall of wooden ships, but in the wooden scaffolding of a new temple that was being built on the city's high hill, the Acropolis. Here, these few people awaited the arrival of Xerxes.

The Greek fleet also went to Salamis. Included were about two hundred Athenian triremes and about a hundred and twenty other Greek ships, triremes and penteconters. These had come from other Greek cities, some as far away as the island of Sicily.

The bay of Salamis was wide, but could be entered only by two narrow straits of water. Within the bay, and nowhere else, Themistocles planned to fight. On reaching the harbor at Salamis, all of the ships in the fleet took down their tall masts and sails, which had brought them there, and beached them. Each ship's flutist took his place on deck, ready to produce the eerie, monotonous melody the rowers needed to keep time as they moved their oars. Each commander took his place, and the marines, armed with sharp javelins, made ready to fight from the decks.

On September 19, 480 B.C. the Persian fleet reached the waters outside the Bay of Salamis. As the enemy triremes sailed closer and closer, Themistocles sat in the wicker chamber from which he would command his ship and whispered in secret with a man called Sicinnus. Sicinnus was a captured Persian who had become a slave in Themistocles' household. Much admired by his master, the slave had been made tutor to Themistocles' sons. Themistocles knew him well and trusted him more than any other man; so he had been chosen to carry out the most important step in the plan Themistocles had made to defeat Xerxes.

That night, Sicinnus sailed out of Salamis harbor on a Greek merchant ship to the place where the Phoenician fleet lay anchored. He boarded one of the enemy triremes and begged to speak with the captain. Sicinnus claimed to be speaking for Themistocles, and said the Athenian general wished to turn traitor and join forces with King Xerxes. The slave told the Phoenician cap-

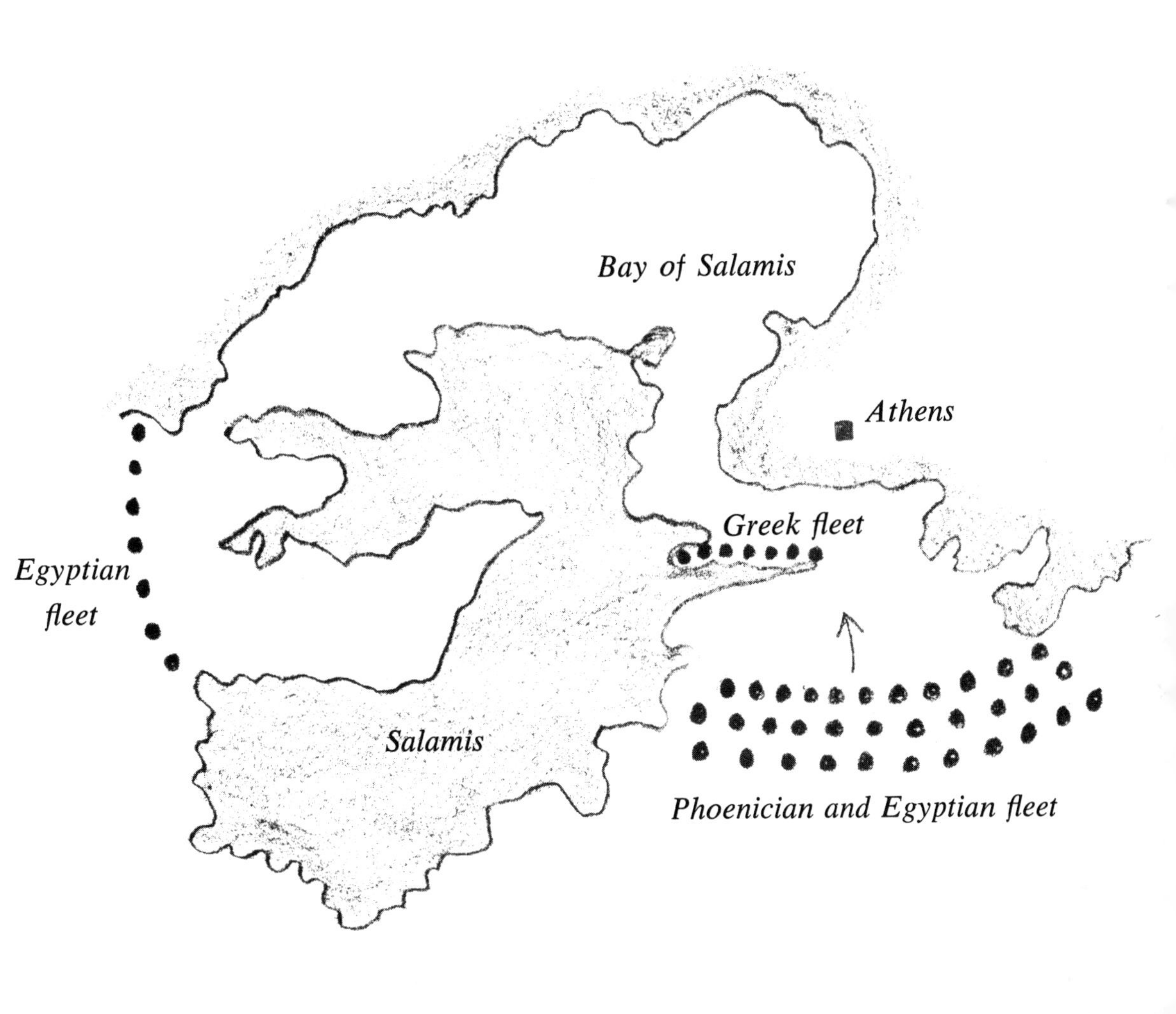
Bay of Salamis
Athens
Greek fleet
Egyptian fleet
Salamis
Phoenician and Egyptian fleet

tain that, that night, while the men of the Persian fleet were sleeping, the Greeks were planning to sail out of the bay of Salamis and escape. Having delivered this message, Sicinnus disappeared into the night.

About midnight, after conferring among themselves, the Phoenicians moved into the eastern entrance to the bay of Salamis, hoping to prevent the Greeks from escaping. At the same time, word was sent to the Egyptians and Ionians, who made up the balance of the Persian fleet, and they moved into the northwestern entrance to the bay.

By dawn the Phoenician ships were in three rows, one directly behind the other, crowded into the narrow channel. King Xerxes sat on his throne, placed on a cliff on the mainland, from which he intended to view the entire battle. A slave held a golden umbrella over his royal head to shield him from the sun, and around him sat many scribes, to record the battle.

Slowly the Greek fleet sailed from its moorings in the harbor to the open waters of the bay, and the rowers began to move their oars to the wailing beat of the flutist on deck. But when they saw the Phoenician ships at the entrance of the bay, they began to row backwards, as if frightened at the sight of the many ships in the channel. At this, the enemy ships advanced farther into the narrow channel, and drew closer together.

This was exactly what Themistocles had hoped would happen. Finally, when the Phoenician ships were as crowded as they could be, but, were not yet into the open waters of the bay, an Athenian trireme shot out rapidly, her great oars churning the water white. She rammed straight and true into a Phoenician trireme, and the battle was under way. The rest of the Greek fleet immediately ceased to backwater and raced ahead, ramming and sinking enemy ships mercilessly. None could escape the oncoming Greeks, for the Persians had no room in which to move; and when they tried, in disorder and panic, to fight back, they only rammed into one another.

From his throne on the cliff, Xerxes wept and groaned in fury. He commanded his scribes to write down the name of each of the Phoenician captains, his village and the names of his relatives, so that not only he could be punished, but his people also.

In a very short time, the battle of Salamis was won by the Greeks, in just the way Themistocles had planned. The navy of Xerxes littered the surrounding beaches with oars, masts, planking, and the drowned bodies of Phoenicians, Egyptians and Ionians. Those who had survived set sail for home, and Xerxes too thought it best to join his army and begin to escape with them by land, back toward the Hellespont.

Themistocles, overjoyed with victory, wanted to pursue Xerxes, destroy the bridge at the Hellespont, trap Xerxes in Europe, and destroy him. But the commanders of the other ships convinced Themistocles that they were well rid of the King. So Themistocles merely sent a messenger to Xerxes saying that it was only by permission of Themistocles the Athenian that the Persians were being allowed to leave.

The vast armies of King Xerxes soon left Greece. It is said that there were so many of them to feed, and so few Greeks willing to do so, once victory had come, that the departing armies had to eat the bark of the trees, stripping entire forests bare, to avoid starvation. Their final defeat was at the battle of Platea where an army under Spartan leadership drove the last of them home.

Two hundred triremes returned to Athens; the people of the city came back from Salamis and Troezen. But however great their victory at sea had been, Xerxes too had had his day; for their city was no more.

Sacked first of its wheat and barley, figs and honey, oil and wine, the nearly empty city had been burned to the ground by the attacking Persian army. The wooden beams of the temple roofs had collapsed and fallen in; the limestone columns supporting the roofs had toppled over. And as the Pythoness had prophesied, black

Athena Planting the Sacred Olive Tree

blood had flowed. The few citizens who had remained behind another wall of wood had been brutally murdered by the invading army, one by one.

The returning Athenians climbed the Acropolis and looked at their holy temples. One of them, called the Hekatompedon, had been a place where the Goddess Athena was worshipped in company with Erectheus, the legendary king who had brought her cult to Athens. In the Hekatompedon an olive tree had always grown next to a sacred spring, where salt water bubbled forth. This olive tree was believed to have sprouted from the shaft of Athena's spear as she thrust it into the soil of the Acropolis, claiming the hill as her own. With horror the people saw that the ancient holy olive tree was a charred and blackened ruin. But then, looking closer, they saw that miraculously, a tiny sprout of gray-green leaves was struggling out of the seemingly lifeless stump. Joy spread through the city at this, for it could only mean one thing: Athena, the bright-eyed goddess, wise above all others, protectress of cities, had not deserted her place at Athens. Here, on this site, she had remained, waiting for the return of her worshippers. And they had come back.

With the sure knowledge that Athena had a special love for them, the Athenians determined to stay and rebuild their city.

THREE

PERHAPS if it had not been for Athena no one would have attempted to rebuild the city. But the Greeks believed that their gods and goddesses were present at certain spots on the earth, usually where there was a cave or hill or spring or some natural formation that was special. The places where temples stood were not holy because temples had been built there, but rather, temples had been built in certain places because the places themselves were holy. So it was clearly impossible to rebuild the temple to Athena in any place but upon the Acropolis, although there were practical reasons why there might have been advantages in moving the location of the city of Athens. Many of these reasons had to do with defense.

When Themistocles had built the wall of wood in the form of ships, he had brought about a drastic and permanent change in the way of life of his people. No longer could they look to land, instead they must look to the sea as a defense against their enemies. Furthermore the victory of the Athenians at Salamis had aroused much bitterness and envy among the other cities of Greece, especially Sparta, and the Athenians had become leaders of a group of people who were not eager to be led. Nevertheless, since Xerxes might one day come again, the Greeks had to remain prepared. And Themistocles continued to build triremes and enlarge the Athenian fleet.

Athens was not ideally situated to be a sea power, for it was about five miles from the sea. Lying this close to the sea, it could easily be attacked from the sea. Yet the Athenians had to go to Piraeus, the port on the sea coast five miles away, to reach their ships. So Themistocles decided to build a defensive wall from Athens to Piraeus, a wall five miles long. This would give Athens defense from attack and would also greatly enlarge the actual area of the city by including Piraeus itself within its boundaries. At the same time, Themistocles planned to strengthen and enlarge the docks at Piraeus so that they could hold many more ships. These things, he felt, should be done before any other public buildings were rebuilt, even the temple on the Acropolis.

The common people were very much in accord with Themistocles' plans. His policy of strengthening the navy had raised the social position of the poorer citizens who manned the triremes. The means by which the city was defended was no longer an army of wealthy aristocrats, but a navy of common people. Most of the oarsmen were craftsmen and working men of Athens; they had been well-treated and well-paid in their new role as military men; they had experienced the joy of a glorious victory without tragic losses. Themistocles had become their leader and hero, and they were willing to follow him in whatever he decided was right. To Themistocles, himself, the good will of the common people meant more than the regard of the gentlemen of old and conservative families.

And so, under the leadership of Themistocles and trusting in his judgement, the common people of Athens, including women and children, began to build the long wall to Piraeus. They built the wall with much of the destroyed sculpture and temple ruins that littered the city. The crumbled heads of gods and goddesses, youths and maidens that lay everywhere were gathered up and carried to the place where the walls were being built.

The shape of the wall was determined by two thin outer walls of well-fitting stones, carved by skilled masons. No mortar was used between the stones to hold them together, so the fit of the stones had to be perfect. The two walls were of varying distances apart, in some places the distance was great enough that a team of oxen could be driven between them. Here and there a long stone was placed between the two walls, forming a sort of partition. Into the shells formed by this masonry, tons of rubble made of small, broken

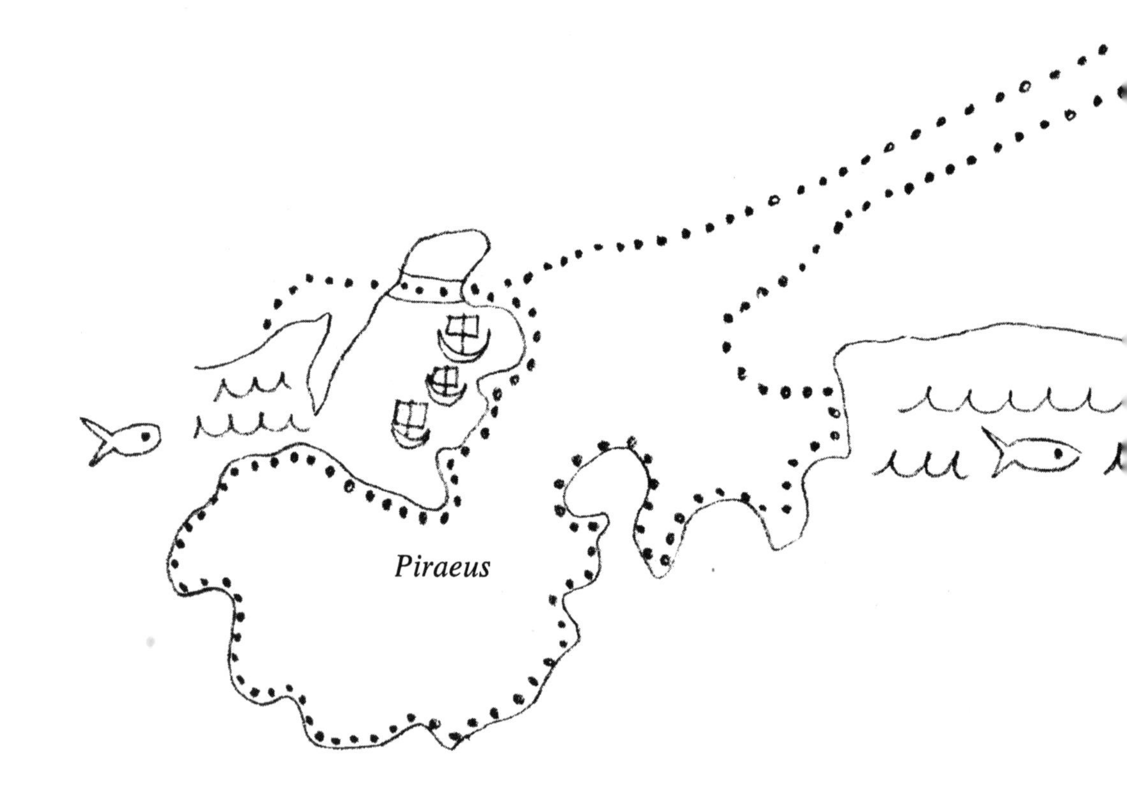
Piraeus

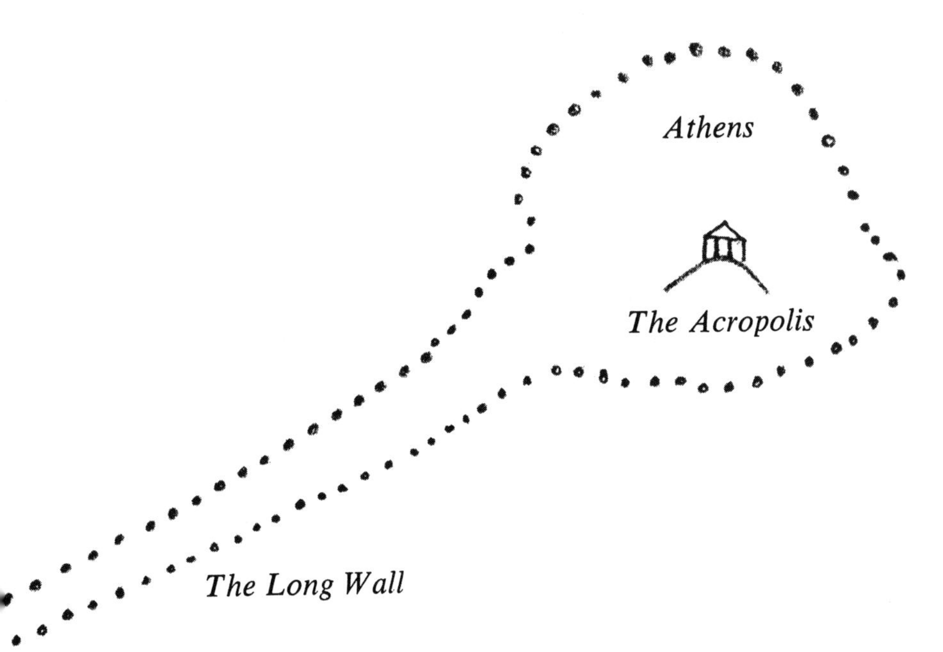

Plan of Athens and Piraeus

stones, were poured. Often, the higher parts of the wall were finished with sun-dried brick. This was cheaper and faster to lay than stone, although it was less strong. However, the upper parts of the wall did not need to be as strong as the foundation.

When the Spartans heard of the wall, they were angry, and many Athenians were, too. The Spartans were angry because they thought the Athenians were trying to make their city more powerful than Sparta; the Athenians, especially those of the old families who resented Themistocles and his upstart navy, grumbled that it was a waste of time and effort to build a wall, for as they said:

"A city is only as well-defended as its men are brave."

But Themistocles believed that there must be brave men, many ships, and a strong wall.

Work continued, while the Acropolis remained in ruins. Before the wall was complete however, Themistocles was in trouble.

When Themistocles had been a schoolboy, his teachers had said of him:

"He will be a very great man, or a very bad man, nothing in between."

They were not entirely right, for Themistocles was a complicated person. He was a great man, but he had a very bad fault; he was arrogant and conceited. At

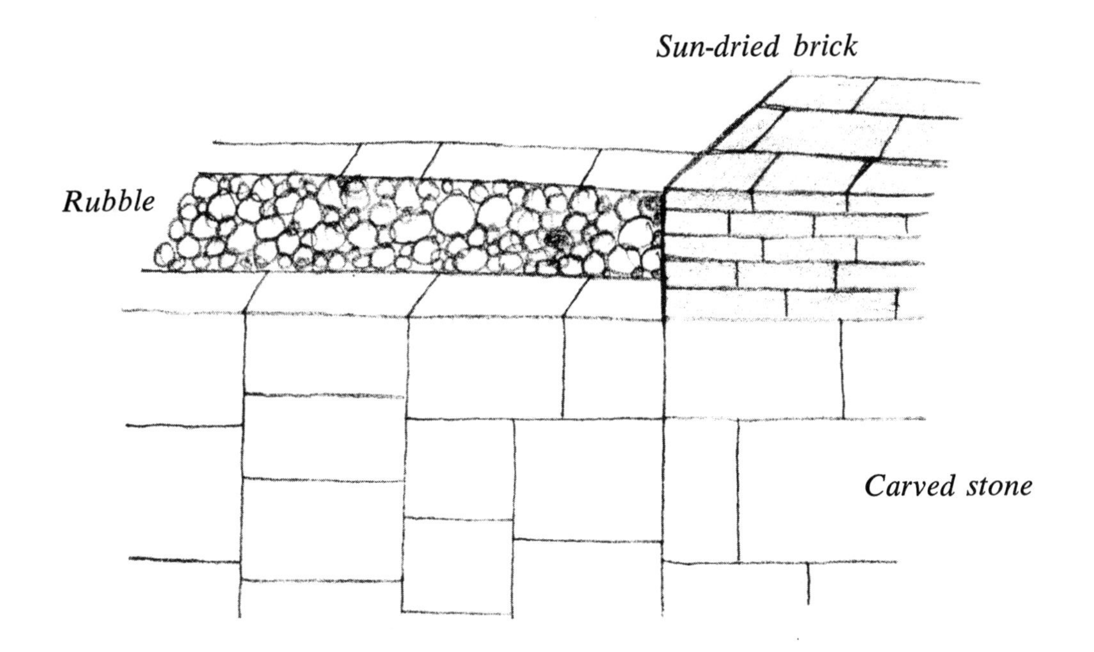

Wall

about this time he had a small temple built right next to his own house, dedicated to Artemis, Goddess of the Hunt. He called her Artemis of the Good Counsel, and he placed in the temple a statue, not of the goddess, but of himself, appearing wise, noble, and handsome as a god. Many Athenians were angry at this, for they took it to mean that Themistocles thought himself better than the rest of them, near to a god in fact. Also, he seemed to be quite rich, and people remembered that he had been a poor man when he had entered politics years before. They accused him of taking bribes. These two things brought him many enemies, even among the people who had been his admirers.

At that time the Athenians had a ceremony called ostracism. During the ceremony, any citizen who wanted to could write a name on a broken piece of a clay pot, called an ostrakon, and put it into an urn set aside for that purpose. If six thousand ostrakons were collected at any one time, the person whose name appeared most frequently was commanded to leave Athens within ten days, not to return for ten years. Usually ostracism was applied to men who had become too powerful. It was a way for the Athenians to defend themselves against tyranny.

At last, when the gossip about Themistocles grew very loud, many citizens met in the agora to cast their ostrakons, and Themistocles was ostracized. He was bitter and angry as a result. He compared himself to a great tree that shades the people when it is hot, but is cut down for firewood when the weather grows cold. Nevertheless, he had to leave, and so he asked the Spartans to let him live among them; but they did not wish to strain their relationship with Athens by welcoming a man the Athenians now called an enemy. From city to city throughout Greece, Themistocles wandered, but no one wanted him. At last he made his way to Asia and offered his services to the new Persian King, Ataxerxes, the son of his old enemy, Xerxes. He reminded the king that he, Themistocles, had allowed the Persians to depart safely after their defeat at Salamis, when they might have been pursued and killed. Ataxerxes agreed at once to let Themistocles make his home in Persia. That night the King drank a great deal of wine and fell asleep. But, it is said that three times in the night he wakened and shouted out joyously:

"I have Themistocles the Athenian!"

Themistocles lived, apparently uneventfully, in the city of Magnesia. He became extremely rich, and in the Asian style he had many wives and children.

In Athens his place was taken by Cimon, the son of Miltiades, victorious leader at the battle of Marathon. Cimon was a brave soldier himself and popular among the nobles, for he represented the interests of the aristocratic families. He was a militant man, and he began at once to demand tribute money from all of the Greek cities that had been allied with Xerxes; those that refused, he attacked at sea.

When Ataxerxes heard this, he decided to try again to defeat the Greeks at sea. He believed that he was likely to win, for he was sure that the Athenian victory at Salamis had been the work of Themistocles alone, the man whom his father had called "the subtle Greek serpent." Ataxerxes summoned Themistocles to him, planning to have him command a navy of Persian triremes against Cimon. Themistocles made ready to meet with the king, but he was planning one last trick.

Just before he departed from Magnesia he gave a glorious feast, invited all of his friends, and sacrificed to the Greek gods. Then, so it is said, after the last guest had gone home, he drank bull's blood, and poisoned, fell dead. Without Themistocles Ataxerxes dared not fight the Athenians at sea.

Cimon continued work upon the walls and planted many trees in the sacred grove at Athens, but did nothing on the Acropolis. For the most part, his time was spent fighting both enemies and friends at sea.

After the battle of Salamis, an alliance of Greek cities had been formed for mutual defense, each city

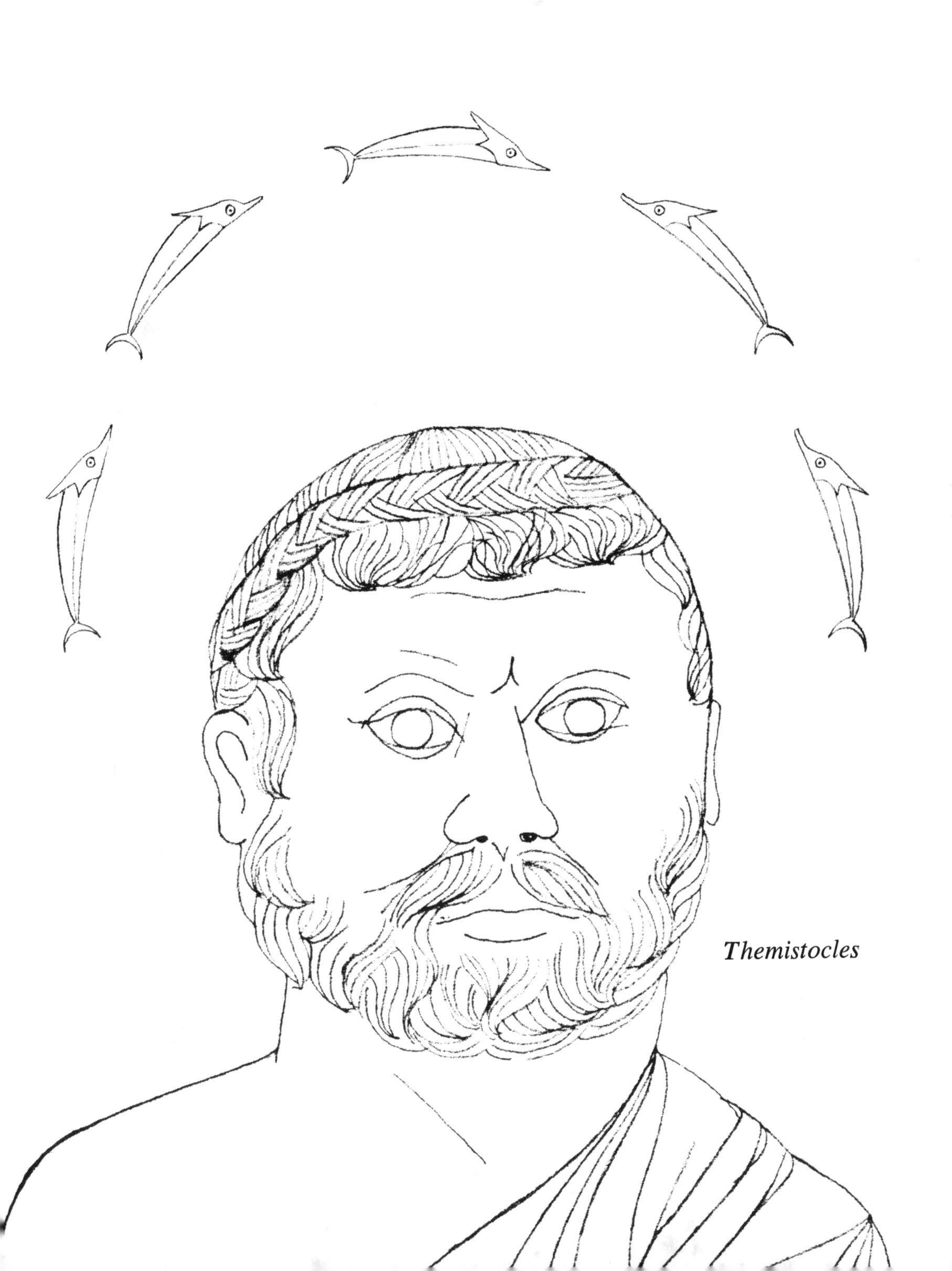

Themistocles

agreeing to contribute a certain number of ships and men. When the danger from the Persians seemed over, however, many cities refused to give ships. Cimon told them this was fine; they could give money instead, and Athens would provide the ships and men. Many cities agreed to this, and a temple at Delos was selected as the place where the money collected to maintain the navy should be kept. The alliance was then called the Delian League. But the cities did not always make the contributions they had promised, so Cimon often went to take it by force.

Cimon was unlike Themistocles; he was simple, honest, kind, generous and brave, although there were many people who thought him a little stupid and believed that he also drank too much wine. The rivalry between Athens and Sparta grew more and more bitter, and in Athens many people muttered among themselves that Cimon seemed more sympathetic to the Spartans, with their rough and simple warrior ways, than to his own people, the Athenians. Certainly he was off making wars as often as the Spartans.

Then in 462 B.C. the many slaves held by the Spartans revolted, and Sparta begged Athens for help in restoring order. Most Athenians did not want to help Sparta; there was too much waiting to be done at home. But Cimon raised an army of four thousand men that set out for Sparta. Once there, however, the Spartans sent them home. They were afraid the Athenians would take control of Sparta instead of just helping Sparta with her problem. When Cimon returned home from this expedition, the Athenians were upset and angry. Once again the citizens met in the agora to cast their clay ostrakons. This time the name that appeared most frequently was Cimon, and so he too was banished from Athens.

During Cimon's many naval expeditions, another man had grown popular in Athens; and the people now chose him to lead them. This man was nothing like Themistocles or Cimon. The night before his birth, his mother had dreamed that she gave birth to a lion. The son she bore the next day was strong and lively, and would have been handsome, had it not been for his strangely shaped head. Its elongated shape, people compared for all his life to a sea-onion. He was intelligent and was educated by a philosopher named Anaxagoras. The boy learned to think well and to express his thoughts eloquently.

Although by birth he was an aristocrat, as an adult he never allowed himself to become a snob, but rather learned to speak with simplicity and grace so that every man, no matter how poor or devoid of education, might understand him. His voice was beautiful, his words made sense, and for these and other good qualities, he gained the admiration of the Athenians. His name was Pericles.

Though Pericles had been born into a very wealthy, aristocratic family, as a young man he had greatly admired Themistocles. Now with Themistocles' power as his own, Pericles planned to do what no one else had been able to accomplish. He wanted to rebuild Athens so that it would be a monument for the world to see—the expression of a free people guided by the wise goddess Athena.

FOUR

To us in many ways the freedoms available in Athens seem very limited. Many common people had no voice in government. The Atheneans owned slaves; and women, however much they were worshipped in the form of goddesses, were allowed no voice in the government or even in whom they married. But for those men who were citizens, great freedom of choice did exist; they did not simply elect other men to run the government for them, instead they voted directly on the issues themselves. Actually, even Athenians who were not citizens had more freedom than most people elsewhere enjoyed; for even those things that seem harsh to us were free and easy for those days. Slavery existed then in all of the civilized world, and there were many people in other places who criticized the Athenians for not being severe enough with either their slaves or their children. It was said that neither knew his place, and it was difficult to tell a slave from a free man in Athens by either his clothing or his manner. As for the children, the Athenians were famous for having children with more curiosity and wonder than was thought good for them; and well-to-do Athenian mothers often hired Spartan women as nurses for their children so that they would learn to be quiet, docile, and speak only when spoken to!

Yet Pericles longed to bring more freedom to the city. To many—especially to those old men of Athens who still refused to wear the new plain, simple chiton that had come into style, but still wore old-fashioned bright colored embroidered robes, who kept their elaborate hairdos in place by fastening their braids with hairpins shaped like little golden grasshoppers—it seemed that Pericles was far too willing to take the side of the many and the poor against the rich and the few. He was, they said, a traitor to his class, a tyrant who courted the uneducated masses, ignoring the better judgment of men born and trained to rule. They were wrong. Pericles, although he was a popular leader, never flattered the common people nor sank to the level of thinking of the least intelligent among them. Instead, he believed that a man was not what he had been born, but what his own thoughts made him. Pericles saw no reason why the thoughts of a poor man could not be noble and lofty, why he could not enjoy and understand such things as works of art, poetry, music and mathematics. Pericles, well-educated himself, believed in the power of knowledge. Poor men, he believed, could acquire knowledge and could help to govern. His ideas did not extend to women or slaves,

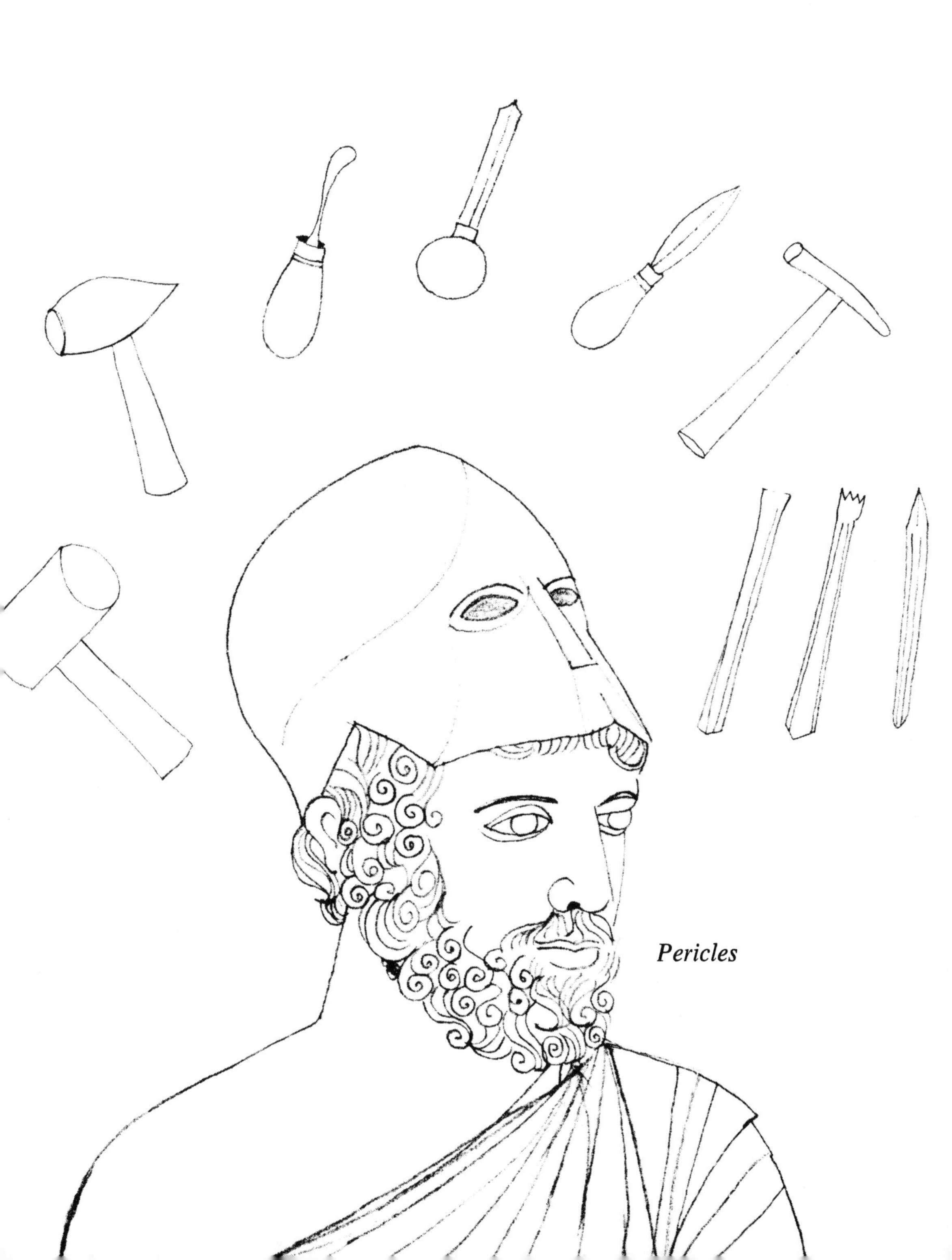

Pericles

but he did want to include many more lowly born free men in government activities than ever had been there before.

Pericles knew that although in theory there was great opportunity in government for all classes, in actual practice, only the rich held office; for only they had the leisure to do it. One of the first things Pericles did therefore was to offer pay to any citizen who held public office or served as a judge at a trial. In this way people who were poor were able to govern also. This disturbed many men with inherited wealth, for they considered it their duty and their privilege to hold powerful office and act as judges while others worked. But this was only the beginning of what Pericles wanted to do for the poorer citizens of Athens. For many of them he had to find work. As peace continued and it appeared that the Persians were not likely to come again, fewer ships were manned for defensive purposes. And gradually many of the rowers of the triremes had come to be without work. These people looked to Pericles to give them some useful employment. He hoped to do this by fulfilling his greatest dreams, rebuilding the city.

Fortunately at this time Pericles had a great deal of money at his disposal. He had decided that Athens was the most important member of the Delian League, and in 454 B.C. had transferred the large treasury of the League from the island of Delos to Athens. This money he felt free to use in any way he chose.

In addition to the treasury of the League, Pericles had other riches to work with. Many years earlier, after the battle of Salamis, the people of Athens had carried home rich booty from the beaches. The fine bronze armor and silver trappings that had equipped the Persian leaders had been taken from their bodies and laid at the ruined temples of the Acropolis as a thank offering to Athena. For years these offerings had lain in piles around the Acropolis between the broken columns and charred statues that still cluttered the holy hill.

Now Pericles felt that he would do something grand and beautiful with these spoils of war. He intended to put them, the treasury of the Delian League and the poorer citizens of Athens to work at the tremendous task of re-building the temples of the Acropolis. He wanted to make the high hill much more splendid than it had even been. He felt this was important for many reasons. He wanted, most important perhaps, to make the citizens of the city proud of the way their city looked, and aware that they were a special people. Then too, he wanted to make the neighbors of Athens, friendly and unfriendly, aware of her strength; he

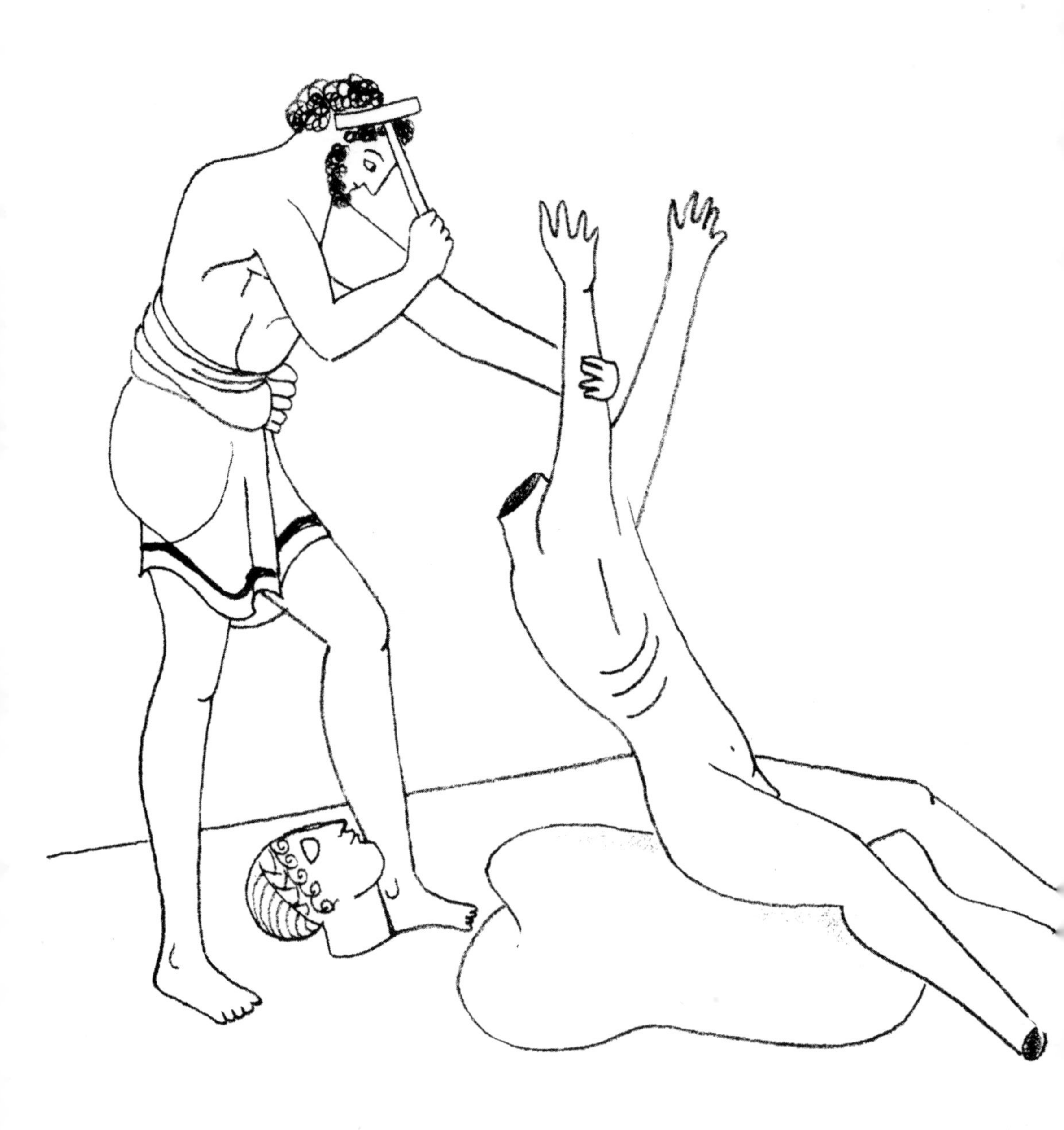

Greek Bronze-caster at Work

wanted them to look with awe at the great city. And finally he wanted to please the goddess Athena.

But work did not begin with buildings. First of all Pericles authorized bronze workers to melt down the shields and breast-plates and swords of the Persians so that his friend, the sculptor Phidias, could begin work on a gigantic bronze statue of Athena to be placed on top of the Acropolis. The statue would stand before the old site of Athena's burned temple, the Hekatompedon, or House of a Hundred Feet, where the sacred olive tree grew. It would be tall enough that Athena's shield could be seen by ships at sea as it gleamed in the sunshine. The statue was to be called Athena Promachos, or Athena the Warrior, and it would represent the goddess in her most stern and warlike aspect, as the fierce protectress of her city.

Little is known of the methods used at that time to cast a large hollow statue in bronze, but it is believed that the first bronze statues in the world were made by Greeks about two hundred years earlier. These statues were cast in many parts; arms, legs and heads were attached to the body by soldering. After all the imperfections resulting from the casting and soldering had been filed, hammered and scraped off, the bronze was meticulously engraved, so that curls and eyebrows stood out sharp and clear. The eyes were inlaid with ivory or white seashells, and an eyeball was added made of silver or glass, giving the eyes a very realistic look. To make the statues even more realistic, the eyebrows were often inlaid with thin pieces of silver, and the lips were inlaid with copper, which was brighter and redder than bronze. The entire statue was polished and was sometimes coated with oil or resin to protect the surface from oxidization, which would change its color from a warm glowing brown to green or black or blue. It is said that Phidias made many improvements in the techniques of bronze casting while he was working on the colossal Athena Promachos, but today no one knows what these discoveries were.

Actually, it was unusual to make a bronze statue of a goddess. Usually statues in bronze were of men and those of women were carved in marble or limestone. It is possible that this was the custom because Greek men were habitually out-of-doors and darkly suntanned, while the women were lighter skinned because they stayed in their houses and courtyards, and when they came out into the open were usually heavily veiled. It may be that Athena Promachos was to be of bronze because as a warrior goddess she was as likely to be sun-tanned as any young soldier.

When Phidias began to create his statue, it was in a style we identify with him. His figures were lifelike, although they were more beautiful than real people; even his relief carvings seemed to have solid form; and his heads had a noble calmness, as if none of the cares of the world could ever trouble those he portrayed.

When and how Phidias developed this style we do not know. He was an older man when he began to work for Pericles and the works of his youth must have been buried somewhere among the rubble of the Persian Wars. But his style was different from any that had existed before the wars. Earlier sculpture was quite stiff—artists had not yet convincingly learned to represent the human body. Earlier relief carvings especially had a certain flatness, for artists did not yet know how to suggest form and depth on a flattened surface.

Pericles must have admired Phidias greatly, for after he had begun work on the bronze statue of Athena Promachos, Pericles named him chief overseer of all the work that was planned for the city of Athens, the port of Piraeus, and most important, the Acropolis.

Yet, as important as the Acropolis was, and as anxious as Pericles was to make it an impressive sight, the first temple begun was one that stood right in the midst of the city, near the agora, or market place. It was dedicated to Hephaestus, the crippled, master-smith who forged the shining armor worn by the divine gods of Mount Olympus. No doubt the craftsmen who were to work on Athena's temples hoped for the help of this god in their work, and perhaps that is why his temple was built first. It was called the Hephaestum, and was built in the oldest style of Greek architecture, the style we call *Doric*. Its plan was similar to that of all other Greek temples.

Unlike our places of worship, a Greek temple was not a place to house worshippers. The actual rituals of sacrificing domestic animals, which formed an important part of the Greek religion, took place on altars that stood outside of the temples. A temple was only entered occasionally by worshippers; its most important function was to house the god or goddess who was believed to live there. As such, it had to be far more beautiful and comfortable than the houses of ordinary mortals. So the Greek Doric temple design had been adapted over hundreds of years from a very ancient and sumptuous style of house.

Long, long before, the traditional palace of Mycenean kings had had a long inner room called the *megaron*. This room had had wooden columns to the ceiling around all four sides and a fire in the middle of the room. The megaron was entered through another smaller room which also had columns to the ceiling. These two rooms formed the basis for temples because

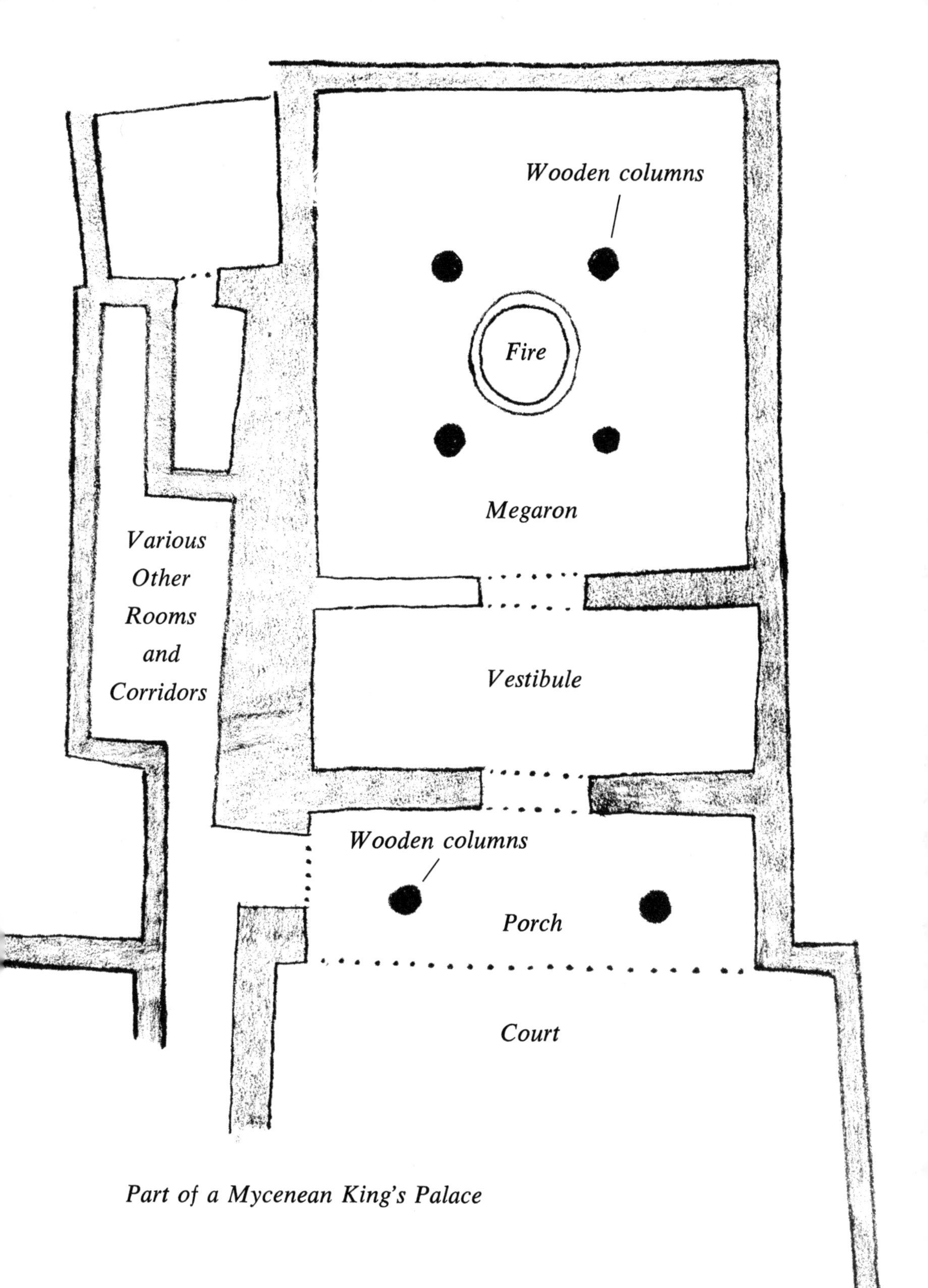

Part of a Mycenean King's Palace

it was believed that if a god paid a visit to a mortal, he could call at the warm and friendly megaron, where the fire was kept, and where the bards sang to kings and warriors.

When or where the earliest temples were built on the mainland of Greece no one knows. The first ones we know about were made of sun-dried brick. Each had an entrance porch, wooden columns at the entrance, and a statue of the chosen deity in the inner room, seated on a throne before a fire. Most of the early temple roofs were of thatched straw, and steeply pitched to let the rain run off. We have an idea of how these very early temples looked because when a king died a little clay model of a temple was often buried with him. These, archeologists have dug up, but no one today has ever seen a real temple like this because they were made of materials too fragile to last through the centuries.

Sometime before 600 B.C. the Greeks discovered how to use roofing tiles made of fired clay. With these, a more gently pitched but equally waterproof roof could be made. The tiles, however, were much heavier than thatch; and wooden columns and walls of sun-dried brick were not strong enough to hold them up.

Across the Mediterranean Sea, in Egypt, builders had learned to create stone buildings and the Greeks may have borrowed the idea from them. In about 600

B.C. they began to make their temples of limestone. These stone temples were larger than the wood and sun-dried brick ones had been and somewhat different. The wooden temples had had columns only along the entrance porch and within the inner chamber, or *cella;* but the stone temples gradually came to be built with a new row of columns outside, all around the temple, supporting the sloping roof and creating a sort of outer porch that extended along all four sides. The porch area formed by this row of columns, or *colonnade,* was called the *peristyle.* It became an important and unique characteristic of the Greek Doric temple. Also, at some time, the ancient builders began to include a smaller enclosed chamber behind the cella called an *opistho-domos.* Both inside and outside, the new temples were larger than the brick ones had been and more complex in their elements. But in many ways, some of them surprising to us, the stone temples carefully imitated their wooden ancestors.

Although a stone column was not quite like the one tall tree that had once held up the roof, the stone columns still kept the vertical grooves that the adze, the instrument used to shape and strip the bark from a tree, had made on the tree trunk. These were carved into stone columns, and are called *flutes.* The rest of the column was also somewhat like the wooden column,

How A Wooden Temple May Have Looked

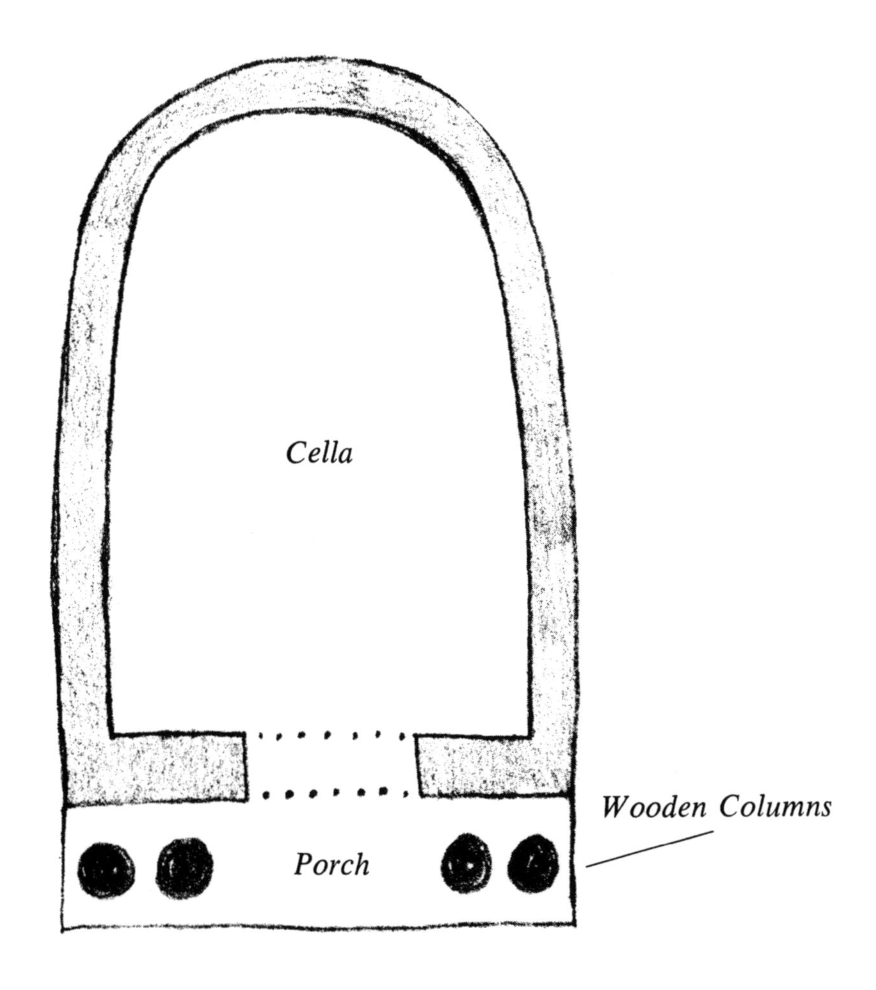

Ground Plan of Wooden Temple

but more complex. The top of the column is called a *capital* and the lower part a *shaft.* The capital is composed of a rounded block called the *echinus,* because its shape reminded the Greeks of a sea-urchin and *echinus* is their word for this creature. On top of the echinus stood a rectangular block called the *abacus.* Between the abacus and the roof there was quite an elaborate section of construction.

Resting on the abacus, stretching the distance from one column to the next, were long blocks of stone. This section is called the *architrave.* Resting on the architrave at equal intervals were upright stone *triglyphs* with two vertical grooves carved in each. The triglyph was supposed to look like the three strips of wooden planking tied together that had been used for the main ceiling beams of the wooden temples. Between the triglyphs were large spaces filled with relief carvings. These are called the *metopes.* The entire band of triglyphs and metopes is called the *frieze.* Above and below the frieze are little carvings called *guttae,* made to look like the wooden pegs that once connected the frieze to the other parts of the temple. The frieze, architrave and guttae together are called the *entablature.*

Above the entablature rises the sloping roof. At either end of the building, this forms a triangular area known as the *cornice.* The triangular space within the cornice was called the *pediment* and was always filled with a large relief carving. Upon the roof, hiding the seams where one tile met another, stood upright carvings called *antefixes*. At the sides of the roof there were gutters to catch the rain; these were drained by spouts at the four corners of the building, carved into fierce lions' heads, whose mouths spit forth the rain water.

The entire stone temple, columns, walls, and interior stood on a stone floor called the *stylobate*. This in turn rested on two substructures called *stereobates*. These three foundations made three tall steps up to the peristyle.

To enter the temple one passed through the peristyle columns, went past another row of columns to enter the porch and then walked through a bronze or wooden door into the cella. Generally a cella was nearly dark, with only the sacred fire blazing before the statue of the deity to light it. At the back of the cella there was usually a small door to enter the opisthodomos or another small chamber that was sometimes included. We know little of the rituals that the priests and priestesses who tended the deity carried out in these rooms, for they were secret and private mysteries, meant only for the eyes of the god or goddess whose home the temple was.

This was the style that the Hephaestum was to be; a great stone building with two inner chambers, an

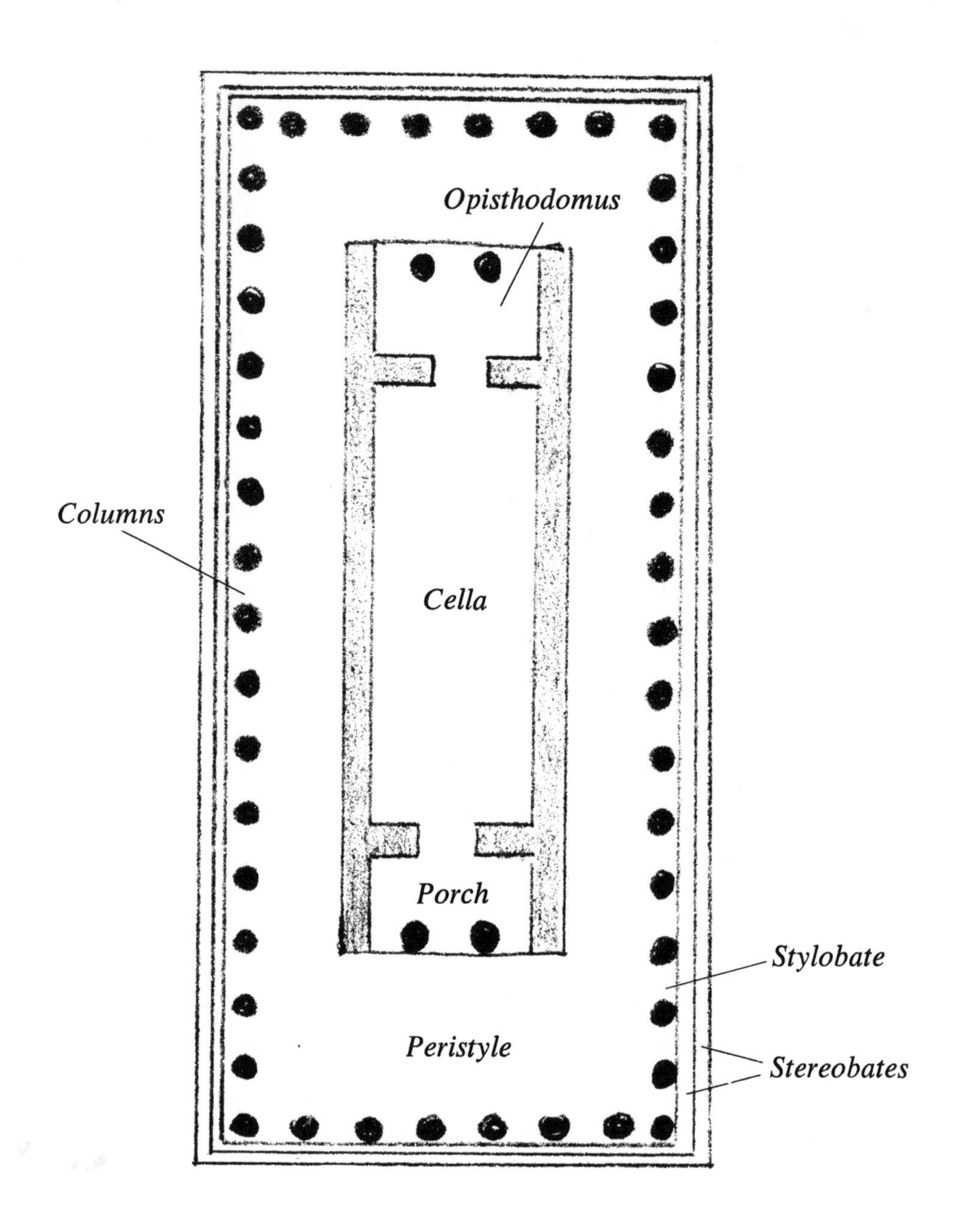

Ground Plan of Early Stone Temple

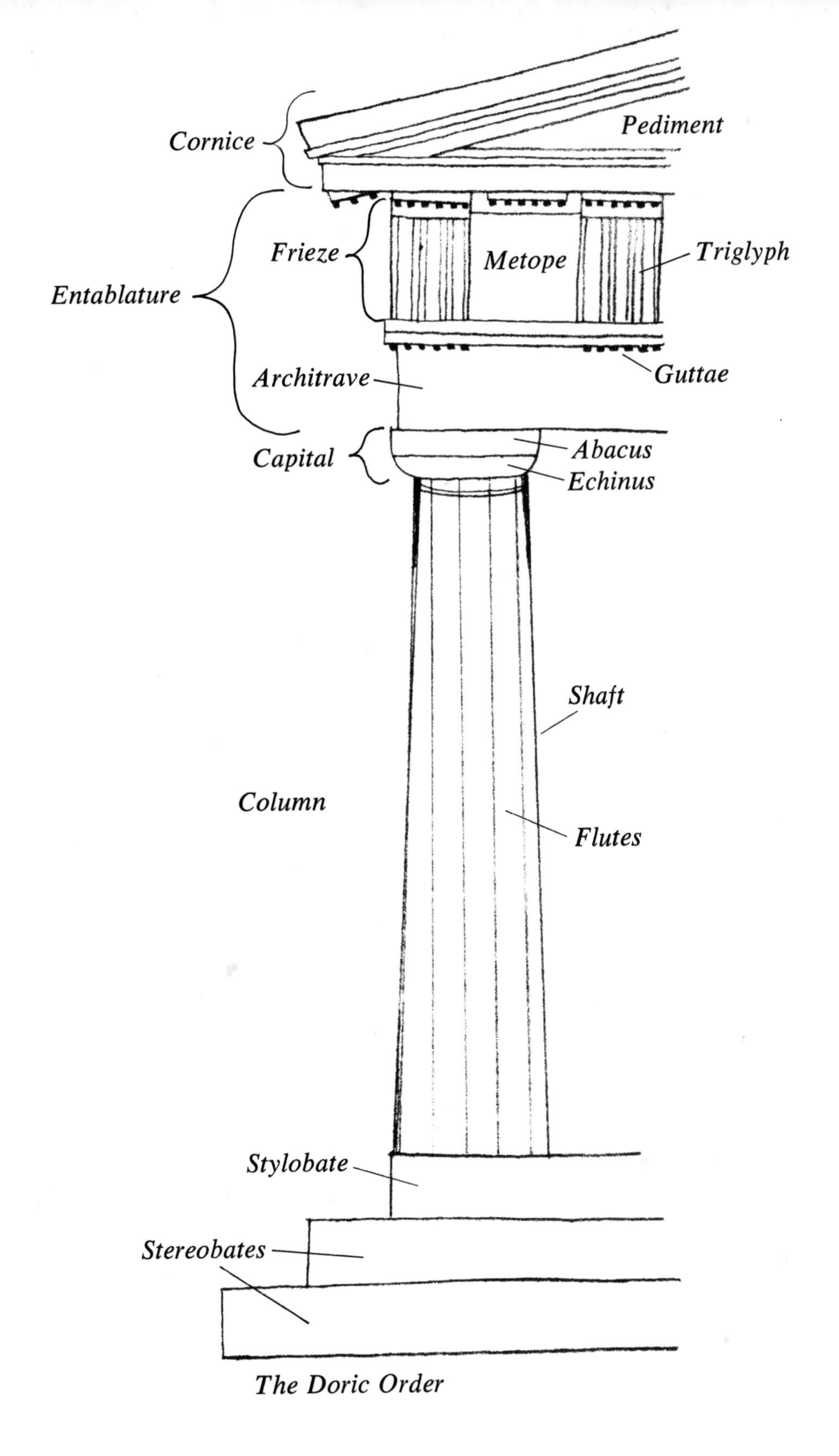

The Doric Order

entrance porch, a peristyle all around the building, and many Doric columns and carvings.

Since part of the building program of Pericles was intended to give work to the rowers on the triremes, they were probably employed as laborers. Skilled work was done by master craftsmen. From the islands of Greece craftsmen of all sorts were summoned: workers in gold, ivory and bronze; carpenters; painters; and most important of all, stone masons.

But the Hephaestum was only a beginning for these workers. The building they were to lavish most attention on, as soon as the Hephaestum was completed, was a temple to Athena. It would be the first of the new buildings to be built on the Acropolis. Since the Acropolis belonged to Athena, it seemed only right that the first temple constructed there should be hers.

Although Athena stood for many things—protectress of cities, goddess of wisdom, the force that made olive trees grow—one of her most familiar and best-loved aspects was that of Athena the Virgin, unmarried daughter of Zeus, the lord of all the gods and goddesses of Mount Olympus. So, it was decided that the new temple would be dedicated to Athena the Virgin, or Parthenos, and called for short, "The Parthenon."

The architect chosen to design it and to supervise its construction, under the general supervision of Phidias, was a man named Ictinus. He was helped by another architect named Callicrates. They decided to use and extend the still-standing foundation of a temple that had been under construction when the Persians burned the city. Only the foundation and some stones carved into shape for use in columns remained. The new foundation was 101½ x 228 feet, and it was situated upon the highest rise of the Acropolis, where it would be visible from the town below. Like the Hephaestum, the Parthenon was to be of the Doric order. Some said that the Hephaestum was a place for the workers to practice building the Parthenon, for the two temples are alike in many ways. But the Hephaestum is in some ways heavy and clumsy-looking, and the Parthenon is the most perfect and beautiful Doric temple ever built. It is the end and final glory of an old, old style.

Although the earlier Doric temples had been made of cream colored limestone covered with a stucco of fine white marble dust, it was decided that the Parthenon should be built throughout with the finest, whitest, hardest stone there was: bright white marble quarried from Mount Pentilicus, which stood between Athens and Marathon.

According to legend, marble had been discovered as two mighty rams battled together high up in a mountain meadow. The horns of one ram hit against the mountainside, chipping away a little piece of stone with a loud, ringing sound. The shepherd of the rams, who was watching the battle, had never before seen stone of such dazzling whiteness or hardness. He rushed off at once to tell the people of the city what he had found. At first after its discovery, marble was used only for carving statues and reliefs; but the architects of the Parthenon knew that marble could be carved with far greater subtlety and precision than limestone and decided that only the best stone was good enough for Athena's temple. So from the mountain of Pentilicus the sound of the stone mason's sledges and chisels rang out, and the blocks of bright white stone were drawn from the earth and shaped for use in the various parts of the temple.

But it was not stone and ancient style alone that made the Parthenon what it was. Much of the Greek idea of beauty was determined by the Greeks' love of mathematics. They were fascinated with mathematics, not necessarily as a useful science, but as an adventure in harmony, proportion, and philosophy. To the Greeks, equations and proportions were in themselves beautiful, not because they resembled anything that could be seen, but because they were purely and simply beautiful in themselves. Pericles' teacher, Anaxagoras, was one of the leading mathematicians of his time, and no doubt Pericles too was well trained in mathematics. Certainly the architects Callicrates and Ictinus must have known and enjoyed mathematics for they used it to arrive at the proportions for their buildings. Much of the beauty of the Parthenon is based upon the Greek idea of ideal mathematics. Ictinus wrote a book on the building of the Parthenon. If a copy of it had survived to our time, no doubt it would tell us much more than we know of how the Greeks designed and built, and why they chose the proportions they did. We do know, for example, that a ratio of 9:4 or 4:9 was thought perfect, and so therefore, there were seventeen columns on each side of the peristyle and eight columns at each end, making the length one column more than twice the width. To obtain the same ratio between the columns, where the bottom of each column was 6¼ feet in diameter, the center of each column was always 14 feet from the center of each of its neighboring columns. Each column was 5.48 times its diameter in height, making it 34¼ feet high. The entablature was about 10¾ feet high, so that the height of the Parthenon from the base of a column to the beginning of the roof was in the ratio of 4:9 to the width of the Parthenon. This ratio was also used in many other ways, ways we do not understand, to determine the proportions of the various elements of the

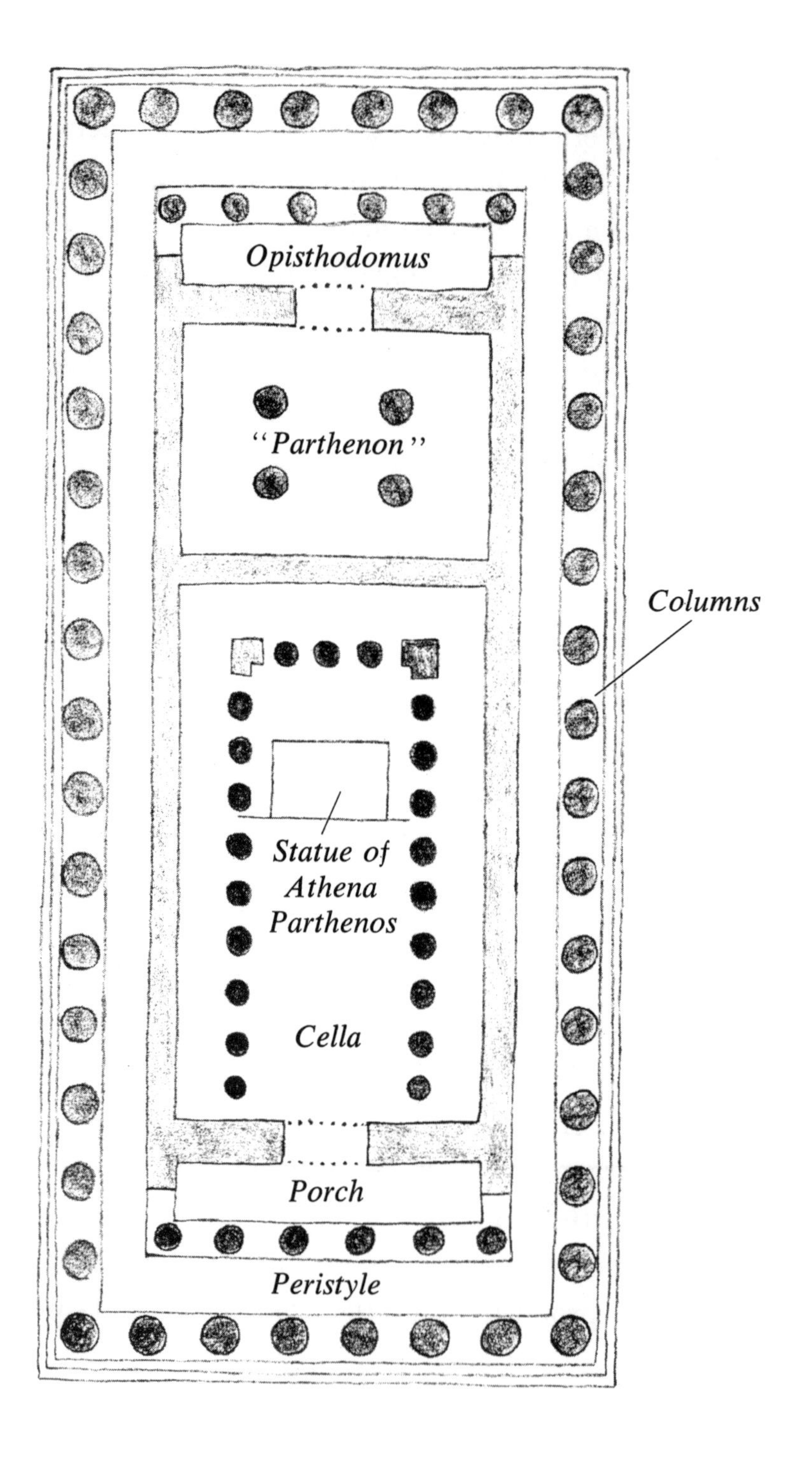

Plan of the Parthenon

building. We find it hard today to grasp how by following this kind of thinking, the Greeks could build a building that seems so right to us. However, to the Greeks, mathematics were aesthetically satisfying; perhaps their mathematics grew out of their understanding of music, which we knew they enjoyed but can never hear, and out of this harmony, came something that could be seen . . . a building.

Once the plans were made, the actual work on the great structure could begin. Since the Greeks used no mortar to make one stone stick to another, it was important that the carving of the blocks be extremely precise. This was done in several steps. The columns, for example, were made of large round blocks called drums. These drums were first roughly hewn into approximately the desired shape in the quarry. Next they were rounded on a lathe. Then they were carved so that the flat parts, at the top and bottom of the drums, fitted exactly the surface they were to meet—either another drum or the floor of the temple, or a capital. This was not easy, particularly in the case of the Parthenon, because the stylobate was not flat, but slightly curved down in all directions away from the center. This allowed rain water to run off and also kept the great surface from appearing to sag in the middle, as it might if it were absolutely flat. Because of this curve, each bottom drum had to be adjusted to fit the curved stylobate at its location; each one was different because the direction of the curve was not the same for each base.

Besides the curved stylobate there were other subtle curves in the Parthenon, put there by the architects to overcome unpleasant optical illusions. A tall column that is equal in width all the way up, for example, is very monotonous. It also appears thinner in the center, though in reality it is not. Therefore the columns of the Parthenon were carved so that they were actually somewhat thicker in the center. This cigar-shaped carving of a column is called *entasis*. The columns were also designed to slant slightly inward to offset the monotony that might result from a long row of perfectly straight columns. The slant of the columns is such that they would all meet at a certain point in the sky if they were continued upward.

All of these adjustments were determined mathematically and carried out in the stone carving by the masons. Each column drum had to have its own subtle shape and fit perfectly to the one above and below it. This would have been an almost impossible job had not the Greek masons had a technique called *anathyrosis*. When they were using this technique, the bottom and top of each drum were made concave, so that the

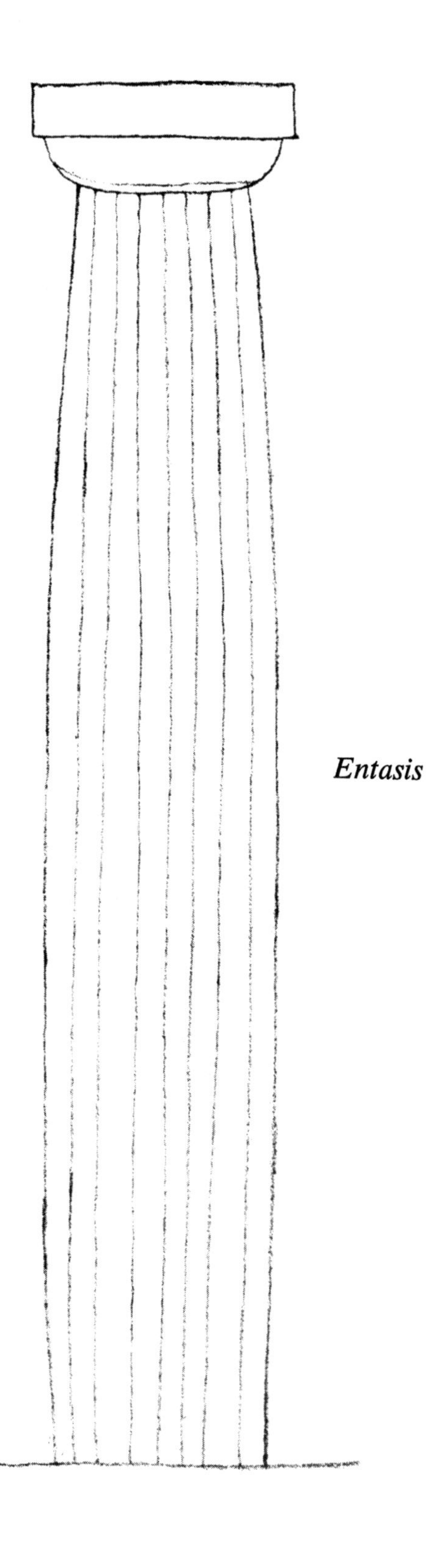

Entasis

insides did not touch the drums above and below. Only the outer edges of any two drums were carved to fit each other perfectly. This fit was so exact that the seams between two drums could be seen only after a careful search. Into the concave center of each drum, both above and below, a square hole was carved. A block of wood was fitted into this hole. Then, a round hole was drilled into the wood, and in some of these holes a round wooden dowel was placed. When the stones were set together, the dowel in one block was fitted into a corresponding hole in the block above or below it. In this way each drum was firmly joined to the drums both above and below.

On all of the large stones used in the temple, pieces of stone called *bosses* were left on, jutting out at the sides. Ropes were attached to these bosses and the stones were pulled up through the air and dropped into place. Later the bosses were removed by masons with stone carving tools. After the bosses on the columns were removed and the entire column was in one piece, the flutes were carved. (This is why, when occasionally today we see a ruin of a Doric temple without fluted columns, we know that the temple was never completed.)

On the Parthenon, the flutes are just wide enough for a man's back to fit comfortably into one of them. The

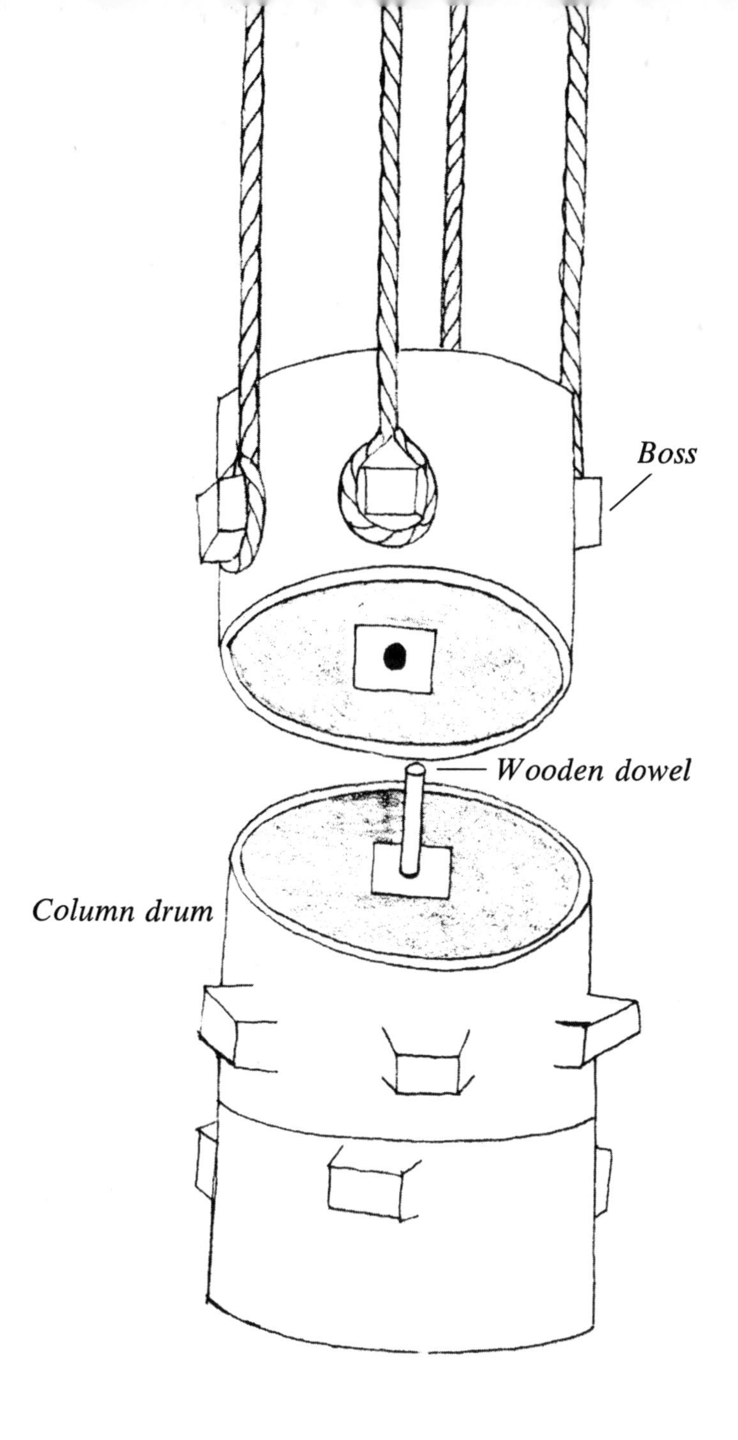

Anathyrosis

Greeks believed that a human being should not feel dwarfed and overwhelmed by a building of majestic size, but should somehow feel that the building had been adjusted to his own proportions. A building the size of the Parthenon might easily overwhelm an individual, but Greek architects of that time held man in high esteem and built, not to minimize him but to make him feel at ease, and yet ennoble him with something greater than himself. To have succeeded as they did was a remarkable achievement, for many buildings of such size lack the human scale of the Parthenon. It is this, perhaps, as much as any other thing about it, that has made it so perfect a building.

Work on the Parthenon progressed rapidly. And everyone who saw it agreed that it was beautiful, but not everyone agreed that it should be built. People from other cities knew that much of the money used to pay the workmen had been taken from the treasury of the Delian League, money that had been accumulated for the defense of all of Greece. The allies of Athens questioned whether money they had contributed for their defense should be used to decorate and glorify one city. But Pericles managed to convince them that so long as Athens provided sufficient ships for the defense of all, the rest of the money could be used to rebuild the holy temples.

As the temple neared completion, Phidias probably spent most of his time in his workshop, seeing to it that the statues he had designed for the building were well-carved by his many assistants. For these statues would be the final glory of the Parthenon. In the metopes around the outside frieze high reliefs (where the carving stands out very far from its background) were being carved in marble. Some showed noble, handsome young men called Lapiths fighting cruel creatures, half-man, half-horse, called *Centaurs.* Still others showed gods battling giants, Greek men battling warlike lady Amazons, and scenes from the story of the Trojan War. All of these metope scenes were taken from stories in Greek mythology, but to the people they symbolized the victory of the Greeks over the barbarian Persians.

For the two pediments of the Parthenon, scenes having to do with Athena were being carved. One was to show her miraculous birth. She would spring, dressed in full armor, from the head and brain of Zeus, her father, while the sun and the moon, pulled by lively horses, rose in the corners. The other pediment would show her contest with Poseidon, God of the Sea, for possession of the Acropolis. Grand, handsome, river gods would recline in the corners, witnessing the contest. These, like the metopes were free standing sculptures.

Metope of Lapinth and Centaur Fighting

Three Fates from the Parthenon East Pediment

For the cella, the space within the temple, Phidias designed an enormous statue of Athena, forty feet high. The statue was not marble, but *Chryselephantine*. This means it had a core of wood and terra-cotta clay, but was covered all over with gold and ivory. Athena carried a shield of real gold, modeled with mythological scenes, and at her feet lay a gigantic serpent she had just killed. Upon the shield Phidias showed a small, bald elderly man, throwing a stone at an Amazon. Everyone recognized this figure as Phidias himself. Another man on the shield, one who was dressed as a soldier, and fighting an Amazon, had a head shaped like a sea-onion; everyone recognized this as Pericles. The statue, once it was set upon its pedestal, reached nearly to the ceiling of the temple.

Though the ceiling itself was of marble, it was coffered as the ceilings of the old wooden temples had been. In a coffered ceiling, beams are placed at right angles to one another to form a square. A flat thin square piece of wood, a coffer, lies in the square formed by the beams. In the Parthenon long, rectangular pieces of marble replaced the wooden beams, and thin flat pieces of marble acted as coffers.

Some say that the great statue was lit only by the fire and by the light that came in at the doors of the cella; and if so, it must have been eerie and mysterious,

Ceiling coffer
Statue of Athena Parthenos

standing so tall, its gold gleaming brightly in the dim light. But others think that there may have been places where the ceiling had no coffers, allowing a soft glow from the vivid Greek sky to filter through the thin marble tiles of the roof above, giving a blurred delicate light. This, of course, is something we do not know. But it was possible, for the Parthenon was the first building built with hand-carved marble roof tiles, instead of the usual clay ones, poured into a mold, and fired in a kiln. The marble roof tiles were very hard and almost transparent. It seems reasonable to think that the architects might have utilized the transparency of the marble to brighten the interior.

For the outside of the cella, inside the peristyle, Phidias designed a long, continuous frieze, unusual in that it was uninterrupted by triglyphs. This frieze was carved in low relief, which means that the figures stood out very little from the background. The subject matter of this frieze was also most unusual for unlike the other carvings on the Parthenon, the scenes to be shown were not based upon mythology but upon real life. They were to portray the festival known as the "Panathenaic Procession," the holiest of all events for the people of Athens. Pericles himself is said to have chosen the subject.

This great ceremony was held once every four years.

At that time a new robe, or *peplos* was woven by the young women of Athens for a very ancient wooden statue of Athena that stood upon the Acropolis. It must have been hidden away at times, because it had survived the Persian Wars. It had been the custom for a very long time to hold a grand festival when the new peplos was given to the goddess. A magnificent parade passed through the city and up the Sacred Way, the road leading to the Acropolis. Handsome young soldiers rode high-stepping horses through the streets; dignified old men paraded solemnly; well-bred bulls, sturdy rams, and young heifers were led through the streets, their horns gleaming with gold leaf, flowers around their necks, waiting to be sacrificed by the priests before Athena's altars. Beautiful youths and maidens carried heavy water jars to wash the blood from the altars, as well as jars of honey, wine, wheat cakes, and olive boughs to offer to the goddess. It was an ancient ritual, stemming from rites that had originated centuries before in ploughed fields, rites designed to ask the goddess who made things grow to give of her bounty. By the time of Pericles, it had become a ceremony of great elegance and beauty, and the animal blood that was shed was of great religious significance.

Perhaps it was because they had become a sea-going people as well as a farming people that the peplos was

Water-Bearers from the Parthenon Frieze

now carried to the statue on a glorious float on wheels, made to look like a ship. The peplos was draped over the mast like a sail. It must have been very richly decorated for almost all of the women in the city did some work on it, and yet it took more than a year to weave it.

It took many years for the great frieze of the Panathenaic Procession and all the other great statuary to be carved. As they were being worked on, the building itself was being built, its great columns, walls and roof slowly going up.

When all of the statues were in place, and the roof covered over with its marble tiles, the statues were painted. On both high and low reliefs, the background behind the figures was blue. Clothing, eyes, and hair were picked out in black, red and yellow ochre. These four colors were the only pigments that Greek artists had available to them.

The building part of the Parthenon was finished in less time than anyone believed possible: in less than nine years. This was a record speed for those times, when all work was done by hand. The statues were completed in another six.

But the Parthenon was not all. Athens was to be magnificent, Pericles directed. The beautiful Parthenon might be an inspiration to all the people who lived in Athena's city, but the city itself must also reflect her glory. The port of Piraeus and the houses where people lived were all to be rebuilt in a simple but dignified style that would show off the glories of the buildings on the Acropolis.

FIVE

PERICLES had gained for himself a popularity no leader of Athens had ever known before; but there were, nevertheless, many people who disapproved of his policies. Because he had the love and approval of the common people, no one dared attack him directly, so instead people made trouble for those who were his friends, friends such as Phidias.

When people saw the colossal gold and ivory statue of Athena Parthenos with her wonderful armor, they did not miss seeing the small, bald, bearded gentleman on her shield. This, everyone recognized, was Phidias himself. Many artists were jealous of the high position Phidias had obtained as overseer of all of the works on the Acropolis. They grumbled to one another that this glory had come to Phidias not because he was more talented than they, but only because he was a personal friend of Pericles. People even said that the reason Pericles spent so much time in the workshop of Phidias was that he was eager to become acquainted with the beautiful young girls who came to pose there. Rumors flew through the busy agora; people even whispered that Phidias had kept a good deal of the gold for himself when he had made the golden trappings for the statue of Athena. Before long he was brought to trial before an assembly of citizens and accused of impiety before the gods and theft of the city's gold. The gold could be taken off the statue and weighed; and it was soon proved that all the gold that had been given to Phidias was there upon the statue. But, unfortunately, he could not deny that upon the holy shield of Athena he had dared to place his own portrait, and so the charge of impiety held.

Phidias was removed from his high office of chief overseer of the works on the Acropolis and sentenced to prison. Some say he died there is disgrace; others think that Pericles had him set free and sent away from Athens where he would be safe.

But even without Phidias, construction went on. In 437 B.C. work was begun by an architect named Mensicles upon the entrance to the Acropolis, a large building called the Propylea. The Panathenaic Procession passed through the Propylea, so although it was not a temple, it must be as splendid as if it were one. It was to consist of a roofed roadway about twelve feet wide and two long sections that were to extend out on either side, containing many beautiful paintings of mythological scenes. The Propylea was to be grand and elegant. Its ceiling would be entirely of marble, painted with designs in blue and gold. And it was to combine columns of the Doric order with those of the Ionic, which were slimmer and more delicate. At the top of the Ionic column, in place of the plain, unadorned Doric echinus, a spiral turned down on either side, with a pattern known as "Egg and Dart" running up and down between the two spirals. The spirals themselves are called *volutes*. The Ionic column also traditionally sat on a base instead of rising directly from the floor, as did the Doric. It was said that the Doric column had the strong, muscular porportions of a well-built man; while the Ionic was tall and slender, as a woman should be.

While the Propylea was being built something was said to have happened that convinced many people, and especially those who had formerly disapproved of the building plans, that the new structures were favored by Athena.

One day, one of the most skilled masons, essential to the completion of the Propylea, fell off of a high scaffolding; the most skilled physicians in the city were called to cure him. All of them said that his injuries were so severe he would surely die within a few days. But that night, while Pericles slept, Athena herself is said to have appeared to him in a dream. She gave him instructions as to how he might cure the injured mason. Next day, Pericles did as the goddess had instructed, and very shortly the injured man had completely re-

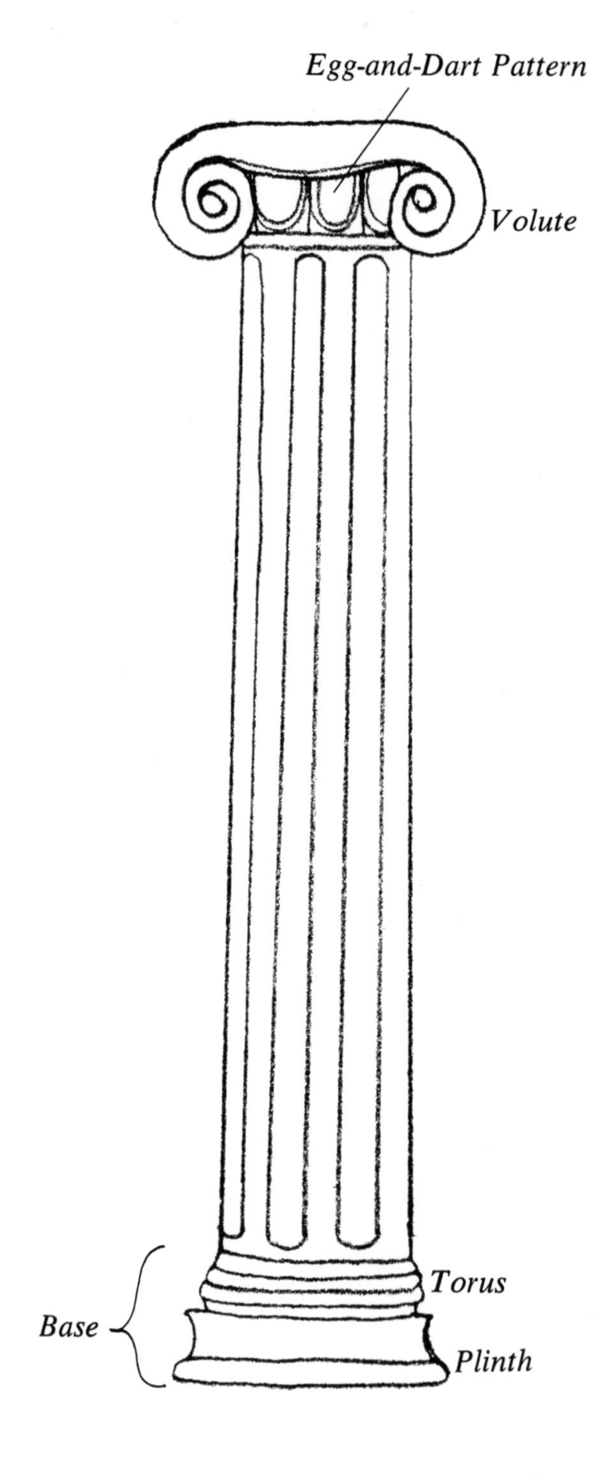

The Ionic Column

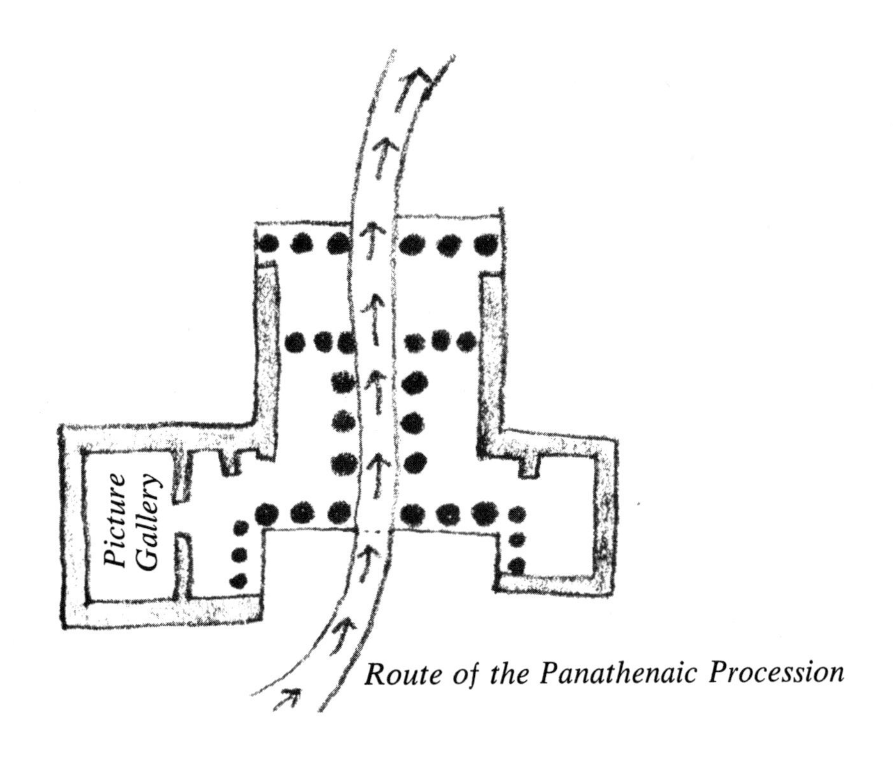

Plan of the Propylea

covered from his accident and was back with his chisel on the high scaffolding of the Propylea.

But, even this much admired miracle could not convince the priests of several ancient shrines still standing upon the Acropolis to move their shrines so that Mensicles could extend the arms of the Propylea as far as he wanted to. He had to make them shorter than he had intended, though even Pericles tried to pursuade the priests to change their minds.

As Pericles continued to spend enormous sums of money on the buildings, criticism of him grew. At one time, having heard too much of this, he assembled the people in the agora and asked if the buildings seemed to them a needless luxury. They answered "yes," so Pericles said (for he was a very wealthy man by birth) that he himself would pay all the costs of building the temples, on condition that only his name be recorded at their dedication. Realizing that then only Pericles would be remembered as having offered gifts to Athena, the people changed their minds and begged him to continue the work, cost what it may, and pay for it out of public funds.

Still, one man, called Thucydides, continued to stir up criticism of Pericles until at last Pericles suggested that the citizens meet in the agora to hold an ostracism. In this way they could be rid of Pericles if they were unhappy with his leadership.

The ostracism was held, but the name most frequently scratched upon the ostrakons was not that of Pericles, but of Thucydides; and so it was he who left Athens, and Pericles remained.

More and more buildings were begun. The architect Callicrates, one of the architects of the Parthenon, was commissioned to draw up a plan for a small temple to be dedicated to Athena the Victor, or Athena Nike. Work began on a temple that would be built over the salt spring of Poseidon, dedicated to Erectheus the legendary King who had, with Athena's help, founded Athens. This was to be called "The Erectheum." But just as soon as work on this temple had begun, fire broke out at the construction site, seriously damaging the stones and the foundation. So work on the Erectheum was discontinued.

And it was not only temples on the Acropolis that Pericles was building. The lower city of Athens and the port of Piraeus also came into his plans. As Themistocles and Cimon had done, he continued work upon the walls. He called in Hippodamus, an architect from the city of Miletus, and asked him to design large quays for the many ships that docked at Piraeus and to lay out new streets so that new houses being built could make maximum use of the available space. A walled city has

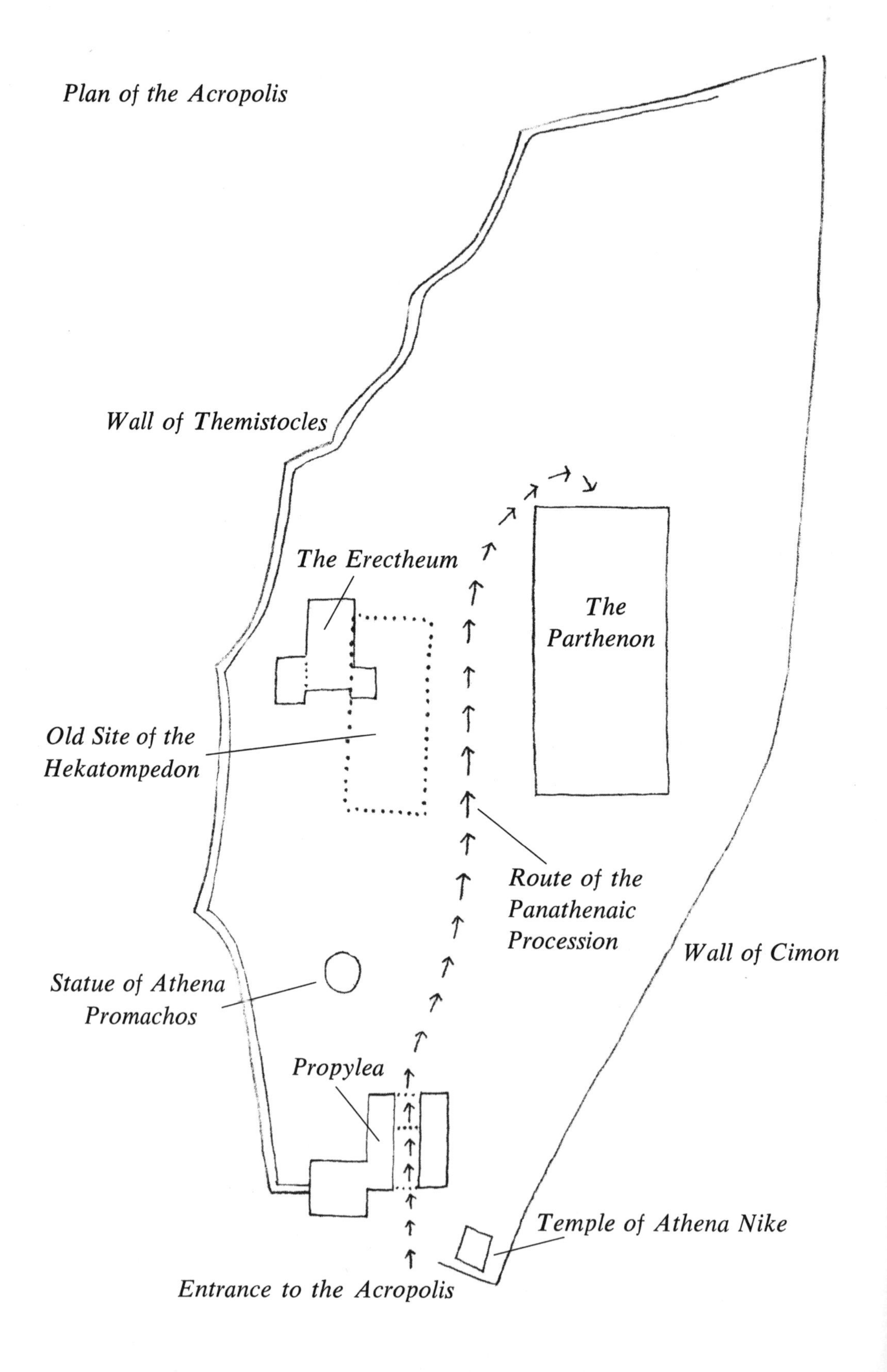
Plan of the Acropolis
Wall of Themistocles
The Erectheum
The Parthenon
Old Site of the Hekatompedon
Route of the Panathenaic Procession
Wall of Cimon
Statue of Athena Promachos
Propylea
Temple of Athena Nike
Entrance to the Acropolis

limited space in which to grow. Hippodamus invented the plan of laying out streets at right angles to one another, an arrangement called the "grid system," still used today.

Compared to the magnificent temples they were building, the houses of the Athenians were extremely plain and simple. They were made of sun-dried brick with no yard on the street and few windows. They were built around an inner court, where the women of the household sat during the day, spinning and weaving and watching over their small children. The houses had no plumbing of any sort, and the furniture was sparse and none too comfortable. However, the people spent most of their time out-of-doors, the men in the agora and the women in the shady courtyards.

The houses of the Athenians were simple and plain for many reasons, but perhaps the most important one is that they chose to have them that way. For it was a matter of great pride with them that their leaders led lives no different from those of the common men and a rich man's house was little different from a poor man's. There were no splendid palaces in Athens, and the people boasted that *their* leaders did not lead soft and perfumed lives in the manner of Asian kings. Instead, their rich and powerful men gave generous offerings to the gods, and adorned, not their own homes and persons, but the holy temples of the city.

Finally, even though the temples to Athena Nike and the Erectheum were not completed, the Acropolis was glorious, and the city itself, with its strong walls, long quays and busy agora was filled with liveliness and gaiety. Merchant ships from all over the Mediterranean world docked at Piraeus. Home bound sailors would give a shout of joy when they caught the light gleaming from the gold tipped spear of Athena Promachos, which they could see before they sighted the city itself, for they knew that they were near Athens. It was a home they were proud and happy to see again, for the Athenians who saw how other people lived, felt no envy, but grew even more proud of their own free ways.

Perhaps the Athenians cannot be blamed for being so certain that their own way of life was the best in the world, but there were many Greek-speaking peoples who disagreed with them. As the years passed more and more people came to think of Sparta as representing an old way of life, and Athens a new. It was true; after the Persian Wars the Spartans adopted an even more severe, rugged way of life; the Athenians, on the other hand, looked across the bright water out to sea, and saw endless opportunity for sharp-witted trade. The Athenians joked about the Spartans and said that they were always willing to die in battle because they

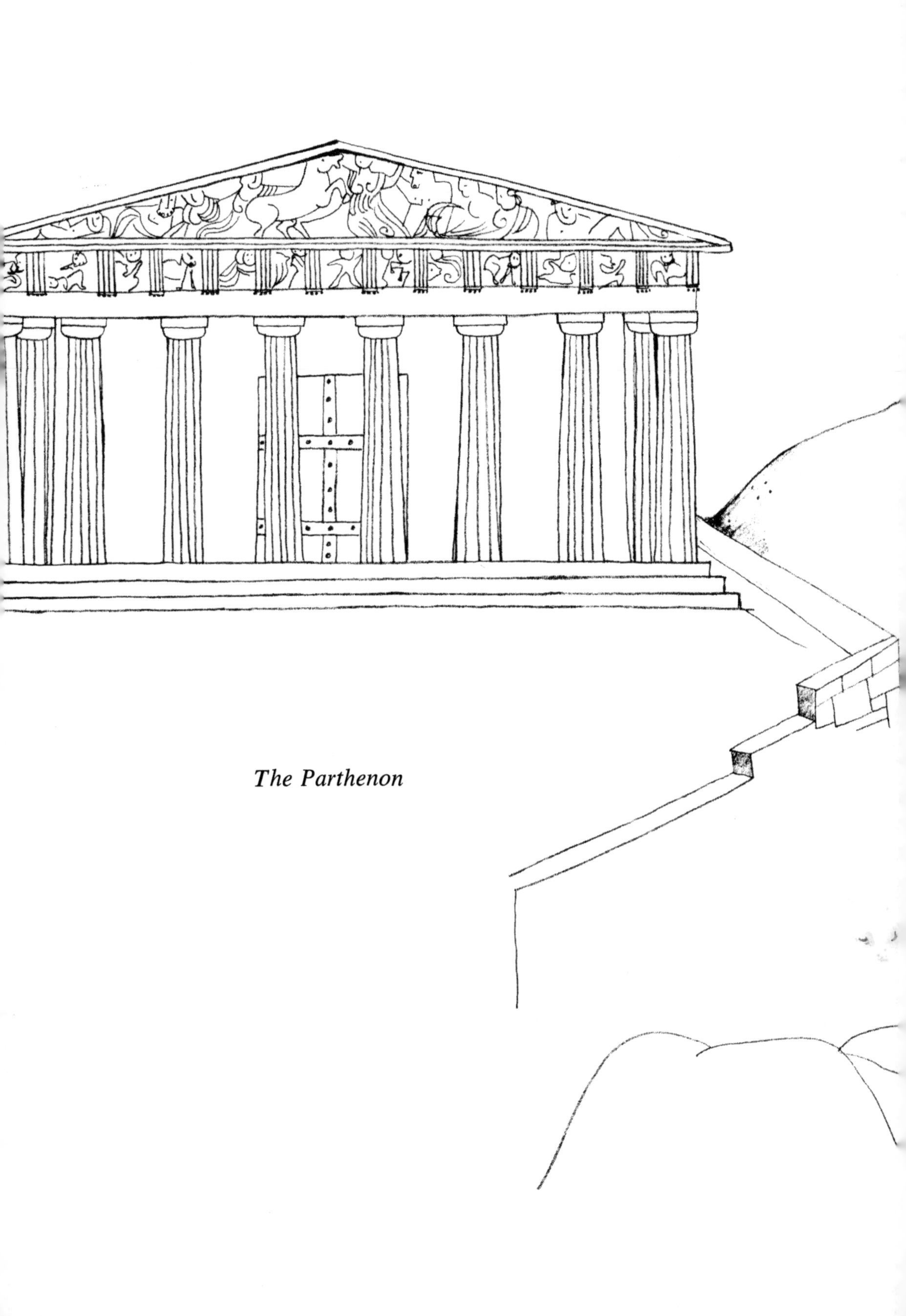

The Parthenon

had so little to live for; the Spartans responded that the Athenians talked too much and never minded their own business. Conservative people often saw the Spartans as representing something old and noble and good, and the Athenians as grasping upstarts. But others, and Pericles was one of them, saw a hardness and cruelty in the Spartan ways, and believed that they offered no chance for a man to grow and discover himself.

SIX

THE LARGEST rival Athens had as a sea power was the city of Corinth, a strong ally of Sparta. In 435 B.C. Corinth became involved in a dispute with the city of Corcyra, which was allied with neither Athens nor Sparta. Fighting broke out between Corinth and Corcyra. The Athenians noticed that Corinth built an alarmingly large navy to fight this unimportant battle. It seemed reasonable to think that the triremes were being built to one day go to battle against the triremes of Athens. So the Athenians took it upon themselves to come to the aid of Corcyra. When the Corinthians saw the Athenian triremes approaching at the time of the battle, they retreated without further fighting, for they were reluctant at that time to fight Athens alone.

Shortly after this, a city called Potidea revolted against Athens. Potidea paid tribute to Athens but was loyal to Corinth and indirectly to Sparta, and Sparta had promised to defend Potidea against Athens should Athens invade. Fighting on land broke out between Athens and Corinth over Potidea, and Athens won. This merely added to the already dangerous rivalry between Athens and Sparta.

Some say that Pericles, certain that Sparta and

Corinth wanted war with Athens eventually, felt that it was best to let it come while Athens was strong and powerful and likely to be victorious. In any case, his next act was not likely to bring peace; for he passed a decree which said that the city of Megara, a strong ally of Corinth, would not be allowed to trade with Athens. The Megarions were completely dependent for their livelihood on trade with Athens, and the decree meant ruin for the people of that city. Megara appealed to Corinth for help, and Corinth acted promptly. She sent ambassadors to Sparta for help. In the speech that the Corinthian envoy made to the Spartans, or Lacedaemonians, as they were often called, he contrasted the two powers of Athens and Sparta, almost, it seemed, trying to shame the Spartans into battle. An Athenian historian, called, as was Pericles' old rival, Thucydides, wrote down the events of that time and tells us what he said:

"You have never considered, O Lacedaemonians, what manner of men are these Athenians with whom you will have to fight, and how utterly unlike yourselves. They are revolutionary, equally quick in the conception and execution of every new plan; while you are conservative, careful only to keep what you have, originating nothing, and not acting even when action is most necessary. They are bold beyond their strength;

they run risks which prudence would condemn; and in the midst of misfortune, they are full of hope. Whereas it is your nature, though strong, to act feebly; when your plans are most prudent to distrust them; and when calamities come upon you to think that you will never be delivered from them. They are impetuous and you are dilatory; they are always abroad and you are always at home. For they hope to gain something by leaving their homes; but you are afraid that any new enterprise will endanger what you have already. When conquerors they pursue their victory to the utmost; when defeated, they fall back the least. Their bodies they devote to the country as though they belonged to other men; their true self is their mind, which is most truly their own when employed in her service. When they do not carry out an intention which they have formed, they seem to have sustained a personal bereavement; when an enterprise succeeds they have gained a mere installment of what is to come; but if they fail, they at once conceive new hopes and so fill up the void. With them alone to hope is to have for they lose not a moment in the execution of an idea. This is the lifelong task, full of danger and toil, which they are always imposing upon themselves. None enjoy their good things less, because they are always seeking for more. To do their duty is their only holiday and they deem the quiet of inaction to be as disagreeable as the most tiresome business. If a man should say of them, in a word, that they were born neither to have peace themselves, nor to allow peace to other men, he would simply speak the truth."

So were the Athenians described by their enemies.

Insults flew back and forth between the envoys of Athens and Sparta until in May of 431 B.C. King Archidamus of Sparta invaded the countryside of Athens. Pericles had expected this and was prepared.

He summoned all of the farmers from the hills into Athens, and their sheep and cattle were transported to the island of Euboaea. Some of the country people moved in with friends or relatives; others pitched tents in any vacant spaces they could find in the city. A few even took up residence in the temples, although oracles had prophesied disaster if the temples were profaned in this way. At last arrangements were made for most of the people to camp along the Long Wall from Athens to Piraeus. From there the people watched the fires blazing in the hills as their farms with their fields of barley and wheat, their vineyards and their olive groves were burned to the ground by the invading Spartans. Looking out to sea, they could see the long Athenian triremes gravely setting sail for the Peloponnesian Peninsula to ravage the towns and cities loyal to Sparta.

When winter came, the Athenian farmers were still in the city. A public funeral was held to bury the Athenian soldiers who had died up to that time in the war. Their bones were collected, put into ten cedar boxes and buried in the most beautiful suburb of the city, the Ceramicus. It was the area where the potters who made the lovely Greek vases lived and worked. One empty soldier's bed was also buried, to honor those whose bones would never be found.

At the funeral, Pericles spoke to the people, and the historian Thucydides tells us some of the things he talked about. His idea of what the Athenians were like is quite different from that of the Corinthian envoy, but both told part of the truth. Pericles spoke not of those men who had died, but rather of the good life that they had died for, and what it meant to be an Athenian. He said, in part:

"We are not suspicious of one another, nor angry with our neighbor if he does what he likes; we do not put on sour looks at him, which though harmless, are not pleasant. And we have not forgotten to provide for our weary spirits many relaxations from toil; we have regular games and sacrifices throughout the year; at home the style of our life is refined; and the delight which we daily feel in all these good things helps to banish melancholy. Because of the greatness of our city the fruits of the whole earth flow in upon us, so that we enjoy the goods of other countries as freely as of our own.

"Then again our military training is in many respects superior to that of our adversaries. Our city is thrown open to the world, and we never expel a foreigner or prevent him from seeing or learning anything, of which the secret if revealed to an enemy might profit him. We rely not upon management or trickery but upon our own hearts and hands. And in the matter of education whereas they from early youth are always undergoing laborious exercises which are to make them brave we live at ease, and yet are equally ready to face the perils which they face.

"If we prefer to meet danger with a light heart but without laborious training, and with a courage which is gained by habit and not enforced by law, are we not greatly the gainers? Since we do not anticipate the pain, when the hour comes we can be as brave as those who never allow themselves to rest, and thus too our city is equally admirable in peace and in war. For we are lovers of the beautiful, yet simple in our tastes, and we cultivate the mind without loss of manliness. Wealth we employ, not for talk or ostentation, but when there is a real use for it. To avow poverty with us is no disgrace; the true disgrace lies in doing nothing to avoid it.

An Athenian citizen does not neglect the state because he takes care of his own household and even those of us who are engaged in business have a very fair idea of politics. We alone regard a man who takes no interest in public affairs not as a harmless but as a useless character; and if few of us are originators, we are all sound judges of a policy. The great impediment to action is, in our opinion, not discussion, but want of that knowledge which is gained by discussion preparatory to action. For we have a peculiar power of thinking before we act and of acting too, whereas other men are courageous from ignorance, but hesitate upon reflection."

He went on to speak of the wonderful buildings of the Acropolis, which were the visible signs of the great spirit of the city. Shortly after Pericles had made this speech, one more monument was placed there. It was a beautiful relief sculpture, carved on a slab, or grave *stele*, of a helmeted Athena, leaning sadly on her spear, head bowed, reading the names of those who had fallen in battle for her city. It was the last monument that would be placed upon the Acropolis for some time; for the following year, in 430 B.C., new disaster followed in the wake of war.

In the port of Piraeus most of the drinking water was rain water collected in wells; for the city was too close

The Mourning Athena

to sea to have any fresh water springs. Early in the year rumors began to spread through the city that the Spartans had sent spies to poison the well water, for many people were becoming ill. No matter how much water a sick person drank, he suffered an unbearable thirst; and most of the sick soon fell dead. Others lived, but became feeble-minded and trembling. The illness spread rapidly and soon reached the upper city of Athens. Here, the drinking water flowed from fresh underground springs; there was no way an enemy could possibly poison them; but people became sick all the same. It was evident that it was not poison causing the sickness, but plague, spreading rapidly from person to person in the hopelessly overcrowded city.

Pericles watched helplessly as the temples he had proudly built for Athena became filled with the corpses of those who had come to beg for the healing aid of the great goddess. And when he stood over the corpse of his youngest son, the aloof and dignified Pericles was seen weeping in public. The plague was beyond control. Pericles sent envoys to the Spartans with offers of peace, but they recognized their advantage over the disaster-struck city of Athens and only pressed the war that much harder. For having led them into disaster, the Athenians suspended Pericles from office, but he was immediately reinstated for the discouraged people could think of no one else to lead them.

Then Pericles, too, was stricken by the plague. He was not killed by it; he recovered, but he was not the same man he had been. He became old and feeble, and he trembled with palsy. A group of statesmen came to speak of important matters with him and found him wearing a little charm around his neck to protect him from evil. They chided him for this, for Pericles had always been above such crude superstition. Embarrassed, Pericles toyed with the amulet and mumbled:

"Oh . . . that! The women must have put it on me."

Within a few months, the man the Athenians had called "The Olympian" was dead; and the city he had so loved was doomed. The war with Sparta dragged on for twenty-seven years; and by the end, the greatness that Athens had known under Pericles had crumbled away. The Erectheum and the little temple to Athena Nike that he had planned were completed after his death, but the spirit of faith, joyousness and optimism that had inspired and created the Parthenon was gone forever. What Herodotus had done for the Persian Wars, Thucydides did for the Peloponnesian War. He told the story, but his story was more grave and tragic than that of Herodotus, for he knew that he was seeing the end of something he loved and admired.

The city created by Themistocles and Pericles was

far from perfect, but theirs was nevertheless a wonderful vision of what a human society could be. The buildings upon the Acropolis were a lasting monument to that vision.

Today we call the style of Pericles' Athens *classical.* It is a style of grandeur and perfection, where even battles seem to be fought in a world beyond suffering and in an atmosphere of nobility and calm. It is a style where real men and women resemble gods, and gods resemble real men and women, but made more perfect. All classical works of art reflect something better and more noble than real life, an ideal to be sought.

Just as the democratic ideals of Pericles have been revived over and over again in the last two thousand years, so artists have often returned to the classical style in a search for perfection. During the Italian Renaissance and during the eighteenth century, both times when people wondered how to govern themselves, the Greeks were especially admired and copied; but never has the classical style again achieved the perfection it had under the Greeks.

Today, the Parthenon, and all of the temples upon the Acropolis are in ruins, and the bright white marble of Mount Pentilicus is a soft cream color from age and exposure. Over the years the Parthenon has been used for many things, and in the seventeenth century the

Turks stored dynamite there. An explosion took place; the roof was blown off; and all of the friezes and metopes of Phidias fell to the ground. Some were burnt into lime, the rest were left to the wind and rain. In the eighteenth century, Lord Elgin, an English nobleman with a large fortune, bought what was left of the frieze of the Panathenaic Procession, some of the metopes, and what was left of the pediments, and transported them the long distance to England, where they were placed in the then-new British Museum. There they remain, in a cold and rainy land, far from their bright-skied home on the high Acropolis, where Athena's olive tree grew.